AN INTRODUCTION TO EXPERIMENTAL DESIGN

THE MACMILLAN COMPANY
NEW YORK · CHICAGO
DALLAS · ATLANTA · SAN FRANCISCO
LONDON · MANILA

In Canada
BRETT-MACMILLAN LTD.
GALT, ONTARIO

AN INTRODUCTION TO EXPERIMENTAL DESIGN

WILLIAM S. RAY, Ph.D.

DEPARTMENT OF PSYCHOLOGY
PENNSYLVANIA STATE UNIVERSITY

THE MACMILLAN COMPANY • New York

First Printing

Library of Congress catalog card number: 60-5410

The Macmillan Company, New York
Brett-Macmillan Ltd., Galt, Ontario

Printed in the United States of America

PREFACE

The writing of An Introduction to Experimental Design began five years ago with the production and duplication of a set of lecture notes for a one-semester course in experimental design given to graduate students in psychology at Pennsylvania State University. Since that time the notes have gone through several major revisions and countless minor ones, and have been used repeatedly in the course with students and faculty from a number of different areas, including psychology, education, speech, industrial engineering, home economics, physical education, sociology, journalism, mathematics, mineralogy, and civil engineering.

It was my intention to start with the simplest ideas and principles of design and analysis, to take up in proper order a few central developments while avoiding many peripheral ones, and to end with certain interesting and advanced topics and issues. In the early chapters I have tried to stimulate students to reason about the basic problems of planning and evaluation. At the same time I have reviewed some very elementary statistical topics. As the discussion proceeds, the sophistication of the statistical approach increases, but repeated attempts are made to encourage the student to integrate common sense and statistics and to strive for a useful and rewarding level of understanding.

In choosing and rejecting topics, in deciding on emphasis and lack of emphasis, I have tried to be realistic about the needs and abilities of the beginning graduate student. Certain standard designs which occur repeatedly in actual practice are emphasized. Designs which are the exceptions in practice, as interesting as they may be to knowledgeable and experienced researchers, or which involve the user in more than the normal number of uncertainties either were not selected or are not emphasized. With respect to abilities, I have tried to keep in mind that my students have been, for the most part, bright and interested but naïve about research methodology and too often woefully lacking in mathematical background.

One more comment about the level of difficulty of the material. It is quite easy at the beginning. It is my own judgment that difficulty increases, at an increasing rate, up to the very end. Some students may find it profitable to skip some of the material in the early chapters. Others, I hope, will find value in the attention given to elementary topics such as symbolism. Some students may find the last chapter too difficult because of their limited backgrounds and the condensed treatment of the issues in the chapter.

Many individuals helped me in the writing of this book. Certain ones, whom I never met in person, did so through their own writings. Others, including a number of my teachers, contributed, in the past, through their lectures. Some who remain anonymous gave me their very perceptive suggestions and criticisms.

Many of my students and colleagues have been a constant source of encouragement.

Dr. James B. Bartoo, Associate Professor of Mathematics at Pennsylvania State University, has been of very great assistance to me as I have, in recent months, grappled with certain of the complexities of statistical inference and experimental design.

Miss Shirley Curran, my graduate assistant, was very helpful in checking the computation in the examples.

I am indebted to Professor Sir Ronald A. Fisher, Cambridge, and to Messrs. Oliver and Boyd, Ltd., Edinburgh, for permission to reprint, in abridged form, Table III from their book, *Statistical Methods for Research Workers*.

Final responsibility for what has been said and what may have been left unsaid is, of course, all mine.

University Park   W.S.R.
Pennsylvania

CONTENTS

AN INTRODUCTION TO EXPERIMENTAL DESIGN

PROSPECT

Experimental design is a challenging subject. It demands and provokes serious inquiry among those persons who aspire to a mastery of it. The part it plays in the affairs of modern man invests it with wide appeal and interest. Its very existence stems from what appears to be a universal desire of man, the desire to control his environment, and, in controlling it, to make it serve his needs and purposes. The study of experimental design is an exercise in thinking clearly and comprehensively about principles underlying the acquisition of new knowledge. This exercise is accompanied by its own rewards of intellectual satisfaction and confidence in research activity.

Man has learned that control of the natural world comes only with scientific knowledge, and so important to him has this knowledge become that he has inevitably turned his attention to a study of the methods at his disposal for obtaining it. The methods employed in the quest for knowledge of natural phenomena are many and varied. They can be classified according to a number of different schemes, none of which is more important than the distinction between experimental and non-experimental methods. One can distinguish a constellation of ideas, issues, principles, and techniques peculiar to those investigations in which the control of natural processes is actually attempted and directly observed. These topics have commonly been subsumed under the heading of "experimental design."

The study of experimental design demands of the psychologist an ingenious use of psychological information, mathematics, and common sense. Of these three ingredients, the psychological information required usually causes the beginner less difficulty than the other two. The student of psychology who is being introduced for the first time to experimental design actually needs to know only a few general principles of human behavior in order to follow the discussion. It is, of course, true that the planning and management of meaningful and important psychological experiments requires the knowledge of the expert in a given content area.

The mathematics of experimental design is a problem for the student to the extent that he has avoided taking the basic courses in algebra, trigonometry, analytic geometry, calculus, and probability theory. Of these topics, algebra is essential, while the others are certainly quite desirable. Even so, the individual who has a poor background in mathematics can, if he is intelligent and highly motivated, acquire mathematical skills sufficient for his needs as he pursues the study of experimental design.

It is the third ingredient, common sense, that gives students the most trouble. *Common sense*, as the term is used here, means sound or valid judgment. It involves logic and reasoning and the use of induction, deduction, or a combination of these in making a decision. It involves thinking in a purposeful manner and finally reaching a conclusion accepted as valid. The difficulty, of course, lies in distinguishing between sound and unsound judgments. What qualifies as common sense and what does not is often a perplexing matter for the student. Having been sensitized early in his training to the dangers of subjectivity and personal bias, he is often unprepared and unwilling to acknowledge that judgment should be accorded the position it actually holds in experimental research. The student can rest assured that any proposition in which common sense figures is scrutinized carefully and systematically by many able and experienced experimenters before that proposition is accepted as a principle. It is also true that much progress has been made in giving expression to these common-sense conclusions in terms such that the judgments are perceived readily and unequivocally as valid. A principal safeguard against the occurrence of unsound judgment in research is the insistence on straightforward and unambiguous language in setting forth common-sense considerations in design.

Appeals to common sense will appear throughout the ensuing discussion without being specifically noted as such, but the student would do well to be alert for them. By detecting these appeals and reacting to them, and by testing his own judgments against them, he will very likely develop a keen appreciation of their importance and a conviction as to their soundness.

Common sense plays no inferior role in research. It gives direction to the activity of the experimenter. It broadly defines the purposes or goals of his work. It provides a conceptual framework within which he can orient himself and make the logical first choice of methods. But common sense is not always exact or exhaustive in its consideration of an issue, and it often profits a great deal from mathematical thinking. Mathematics, mathematical statistics, or statistics—whatever the term one prefers—provides a complete and exact specification of the assumptions and the deductions underlying the objective and standard methods of evaluation. This specification of the terms and conditions of an exact evaluation has implications for the planning phase of experimentation. It is evident that one should plan initially so that the desired final evaluation can be accomplished legitimately.

Here common sense comes again into play. It is a matter of judgment as to what constitutes an adequate implementation or realization of the terms and conditions specified by the mathematics. Perfection in fulfilling the requirements is never knowingly attained. Some deviation from the ideal is taken as inevitable and unavoidable. It seems reasonable, then, to give attention to the consequences of failures in fulfilling the requirements of the evaluation. Knowing the consequences and their seriousness provides a basis for judging the adequacy of implementation and a context within which the judgment can be defended or criticized.

The beginning psychologist will encounter many intellectual chores in the study of experimental design. He must think about issues for which his previous experience typically provides little background. He must continue to react to these issues and attempt to invest them with meaning until a context or frame of reference for them gradually comes into being. He must struggle to divest himself of old, inadequate ways of thinking and speaking, and force himself to use unfamiliar words and phrases in an effort to establish and express new concepts. He must attend very closely to the language employed in experimental design and exact of himself a similar, careful choice of language. He must strive for clarity, directness, and unambiguity of thought and expression.

It is a frustrating and discouraging experience to flounder about blindly in one's efforts to deal with problems of experimentation, as many an individual does before he has the opportunity to study experimental design. On the other hand, having the conviction that one is thinking clearly and communicating effectively about these problems is a highly gratifying experience for the person who has had the opportunity and been willing to pay the price of concentration and sustained effort.

OBJECTIVES AND SCOPE

The subject matter of experimental design consists of many variations on a few central themes. In his first course, the student needs to have the main themes delineated and explained. He can fill in many of the variations later, on his own, as he continues to advance in knowledge of his field and accumulate experience in research. Early preoccupation with minor or peripheral issues only hinders his learning of the essentials and limits his view of the whole.

The principal issues which the present introduction to experimental design attempts to cover are the following:

(1) The logic of the comparisons provided by a design. It is important for the experimenter to be able to conceptualize for himself and to communicate to others the basic nature and meaning of the arithmetic manipulations he undertakes with his data. In the simplest designs, the nature of the experimental comparisons is easily understood and does not require an extended explanation. In the more comprehensive factorial designs, however, and in the designs involving curve-fitting, the comparisons merit and receive a detailed description.

(2) Validity and precision, the two objectives of all experimentation. The statistical tests of significance employed throughout the text are those appropriate to the analysis of variance or covariance. These tests are based on what is known as *normal curve theory*. Consequently, the conditions on which validity depends are described by reference to the assumptions of normal curve theory and the consequences of failure in the assumptions. Matching and adjusting procedures are presented as ways of increasing the precision of a design.

(3) Computation. An attempt has been made to structure the general computing procedures so that the student can readily carry out the computation and verify his understanding of each method of analysis. For the most part, artificial data have been employed in the computing examples. Artificial data have been synthesized to render the arithmetic simple. It is quite feasible to perform the analyses for the examples by paper-and-pencil methods without recourse even to a desk calculator. Under these conditions, verifying the computations should not seriously disrupt the flow of thought and the development of understanding.

It is only fair to the student and his teacher to acknowledge in advance that certain topics have been deliberately omitted. Only brief reference will be made to nonparametric tests of significance. Emphasis will be placed on the analysis of variance and covariance because they constitute an excellent point of departure for conceptualizing problems of design in terms of components or sources of variability. Furthermore, the analysis of variance and covariance can be applied to a great variety of designs with only minor variations in computing. Finally, it should be pointed out that the basic issues regarding experimental comparisons and the major ways of achieving validity and precision are much the same regardless of the choice of a statistic for evaluation.

Statisticians often distinguish two principal uses of inference. They are the testing of significance and the estimating of parameters. The problem of evaluation is formulated and solved here only in terms of tests of significance. No attention is given to estimation. It is, regrettably, a fact that psychologists seldom use estimation in experimental research. The reason, however, is clear and understandable. They are, in most cases, involved in exploratory research affected by large errors, a situation in which rejection of the null hypothesis in a test of significance is a fairly high aspiration. The usually arbitrary nature of the scale units in which observations are expressed in psychology also reduces the meaningfulness of estimation. Perhaps the time will come when estimating parameters will be as important in psychology as it is in certain other fields where measurement and the control of biasing errors are further advanced.

One additional point should be made by way of indicating the scope of the present discussion. Designs can be classified according to the kinds of random variation assumed to be operating in the experiment. For the most part, the designs we shall consider involve error variation arising from the selection, assigning, and measuring of experimental materials. We shall discuss only a few designs in which random selection of the experimental conditions introduces an additional source of error. Except in the simplest cases, these so-called *components-of-variance* designs or *random effects* designs involve difficulties of interpretation which are likely to go beyond the capabilities of beginning students.

FUNDAMENTALS

2

An experiment is a formal event in the scientist's continuing quest for knowledge. In designing and undertaking his investigations the scientist typically poses questions and, at the same time, advances hypotheses as to the answers he expects to find. An experiment is an event planned and staged by him to yield evidence relevant to one or more of his hypotheses. Evidence of a confirming or positive nature, as it accumulates in many repetitions of an experiment, eventually constitutes a contribution to our knowledge.

In the conduct of an experiment the scientist is active. He controls, manipulates, and observes. In a sense, he is an interventionist, one who deliberately and systematically introduces changes into natural processes and then observes the consequences of those changes. In certain other kinds of research of a nonexperimental character, he is a passive observer who is interested in recording the behavior of objects or organisms in a relatively undisturbed natural setting.

The hypotheses of the experimenter express his expectations as to the changes which will result from the changes he initiates. He controls certain variables, manipulates one or more others, and then makes careful observations of the effect of the manipulation on still another variable.

EXPERIMENTAL MANIPULATION

As it is used here, the word "manipulation" has a quite specific meaning. Manipulation of a variable is an operation performed by the experimenter. The manipulation is physical, not conceptual. It is objective, not subjective. It is real, not imaginary. It necessitates an overt action on the part of the experimenter. It cannot be achieved covertly in the thought processes of the investigator.

6

In several fields of research, including psychology and the other behavioral sciences, the manipulation of a variable takes a characteristic form in which the investigator imposes different conditions on his experimental materials. In psychological research, the experimental materials are living organisms—animal or human subjects—and the varied conditions are imposed on these organisms by the investigator.

To say, then, that a psychologist manipulates a variable means that he imposes a set of varied conditions on his subjects. The set of varied conditions is referred to as the *independent* variable, the *experimental* variable, or the *treatment* variable. Differences among the conditions themselves may be quantitative or qualitative; that is, they may be differences in degree or differences in kind. When they are differences in degree, we speak of *levels* of treatment. When they are differences in kind, we speak of *qualities* of treatment.

Listed below are examples of independent variables taken from psychological research. Each independent variable is a set of conditions which can be imposed by the psychologist on his animal or human subjects.

1. The number of trials allowed in traversing a maze.
2. The number of hours of food deprivation.
3. The amount of sedation administered.
4. The number of hours of psychotherapy given.
5. The intensity of an auditory stimulus.
6. Instructions for taking a projective test.
7. The ratio of the length of the major axis to the length of the minor axis of an ellipse presented as a visual stimulus.

OBSERVATION OF RESPONSE

In psychological experimentation we are interested in the effect of the manipulation of the independent variable(s) on a response variable. Observations are made with respect to some characteristic of the behavior of the subjects employed in the research. These observations are usually, but not always, of a quantitative sort. This measure of effect is called the *dependent* variable, the *criterion* variable, and, in nonpsychological literature, the *yield*. We prefer "dependent variable" and will continue to employ that term.

Listed below are examples of dependent variables taken from psychological research. Each dependent variable is a response characteristic which can be measured by the psychologist.

1. Latency of response in word association.

2. Absolute threshold for identification of a visual stimulus.
3. Score on an attitude scale.
4. Number of items correct on a psychological test.
5. Number of errors made in traversing a maze.
6. Number of revolutions of an activity wheel.
7. Number of words recalled from a list.

DIFFERENCES AMONG SUBJECTS

There is a very general property of response variables that, as we shall see later on, creates a problem for the psychologist in the planning, execution, and evaluation of an experiment. When measures of the responses of a number of human subjects are obtained under uniform conditions for all subjects, these measures typically display variability. The same is true for animal subjects. That is to say, responses vary from one person to another or from one animal to another, even under the same conditions of measurement. The variation in the responses is represented in the observable differences in the obtained measures.

The casual observer might be quite willing to attribute the variability of measures of response entirely to errors of measurement, that is, to influences of a momentary and transitory nature within the subject and in the environment surrounding him at the time the measurement of his response is obtained. The evidence, with which psychologists have long been familiar, refutes this view. The evidence is that these differences among individual subjects are relatively stable. The tendency for these differences to persist from one occasion of measurement to another does, of course, vary. That is to say, the differences among individuals are sometimes large and sometimes small, depending upon the group of individuals, the characteristic of response being measured, and the adequacy of the measuring instrument. Theoretically, there is nothing to prevent our discovering a response variable on which all individuals obtain the same measurement. Actually, stable differences among individuals have been found so often in so many varied areas that the tendency for observed differences to persist has become a criterion of reproducibility or reliability in psychological measurement. The linear correlation between measures obtained from the same subjects on two different occasions is commonly used to describe this tendency and to express the extent of individual differences.

Differences among subjects represent for the psychologist what is described by experimenters in general as *heterogeneity* of experimental materials. We shall see that the heterogeneity of experimental materials poses a basic problem for the investigator in interpreting the results of his experiments.

THE EXPERIMENTAL COMPARISON

We shall now introduce some symbols to represent the elements of the experimental situation as they have been discussed up to this point. A group of subjects will be represented by a square, or by a rectangle when it is convenient. Each condition imposed by the experimenter on a group of subjects will be represented by a single, capital, italic Latin letter.

For the simplest experiment, two groups of subjects and two conditions will be required. Let us suppose that two qualitatively different conditions, A and B, are to be employed in the experiment. The imposition of treatments on the two groups of subjects can then be symbolized as

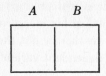

After the experimenter has imposed the conditions on his subjects, he makes a measurement on each subject on the dependent variable. We shall use either Y_{ia} or Y_{ib} for a measure of response. The subscript, i, indicates the possibility of identifying any individual in a given group. The subscript, a or b, identifies the group in terms of the treatment it receives. That is, Y_{ia} refers to the observation on the ith individual in the group receiving treatment A, and Y_{ib} refers to the observation on the ith individual in the group receiving treatment B. The experiment can now be represented as

$$A \qquad B$$

$$\boxed{\quad Y_{ia} \quad | \quad Y_{ib} \quad}$$

The next step is the evaluation. Is there a difference between the two groups? Is the effect of treatment A different from that of treatment B?

Has the effect of treatment *A* been such as to produce responses different from those produced by the effect of treatment *B*? These are varying forms of the question which the experimenter now asks. The question implies and requires a comparison of the measures of response in the one group with the measures of response in the other group. The comparison should tell the experimenter whether or not differences on the dependent variable, *Y*, the measure of response, are associated with differences on the independent variable as represented by the two different conditions, *A* and *B*.

For reasons which will soon be presented and discussed, it is not usually a simple matter to reach a satisfactory conclusion as to the outcome of an experiment. Before considering these reasons, let us review briefly the discussion as it has developed thus far.

The experimenter states a question for which he seeks an answer. The question is concerned with the relation between a response variable and a treatment variable. He advances a hypothesis as to the nature of the relation between the two variables. In other words, he states an expectation that the difference in conditions will produce differences in response. He imposes the conditions and makes his measurements. He has his data at hand. Now he must decide whether or not there is a relation between the independent variable and the dependent variable.

THE PROBLEM OF EVALUATION

The decision as to the outcome of an experiment is seldom an easy one to make on the basis of a mere inspection of the data. As an example of the difficulty the investigator encounters, let us examine the data from an actual experiment in psychology.[1] In the experiment chosen as an example, the response variable was a measure of cheating. Children in one group, referred to as the *control* group by the experimenter, were given instructions in scoring their own tests and were told not to change their answers. Children in a second group, called the *reward* group by the experimenter, were given instructions in scoring their own tests, were told not to change their answers, and were promised a reward if they carried out the instructions properly. Children in both groups were then allowed to score their own tests without supervision. A *cheating score* for a single child was defined as the difference between the score the child gave himself and his actual score, as determined by the experimenter. The cheating scores obtained by the 19 children in the control group and the 18 children in the reward group are presented in Table 2.1.

Table 2.1
SCORES FOR TWO GROUPS OF CHILDREN
IN THE EXPERIMENT ON CHEATING

Control group	Reward group
4	4
6	1
11	15
13	3
5	0
2	5
7	8
0	2
2	0
0	−1
0	0
11	1
0	0
0	0
1	0
1	0
6	0
10	−1
0	

The experimenter's hypothesis was that the children who had been promised a reward would cheat less than the children in the other group. Is this hypothesis supported by the observations? Is there a difference between the two groups in amount of cheating? Let us examine the scores.

We observe that there were children in both groups who had scores of zero. Six children in the control group and eight in the reward group had such scores. We note, too, that two children in the reward group actually gave themselves scores one point lower than their actual scores. It is also true that several of the higher scores are found in the control group. These characteristics of the observations appear to support the investigator's hypothesis that the promise of a reward would diminish the amount of cheating. We should point out, however, that "15", the highest cheating score of all, is found in the reward group.

Before trying to reach a final conclusion as to the results, we should question the manner of composing the two groups of subjects. How were children assigned to the two different conditions? In examining the data, we observe that there are large differences among the scores within each group. The presence of these differences suggests that the children differed in either opportunity or propensity to cheat in a situation of the kind structured by the experimenter. Is it possible that, in assigning the children to the two groups, one condition was favored over the other? It may be that the control group happened to have placed in it children who either could or would cheat more than the children placed in the other group. If so, the apparent effect of the promise of reward can be explained in terms of differences between the groups before the experimental conditions were even imposed. The obtained cheating scores may reflect only initial differences between the groups and not the differential effects of the instructions. We see, then, that the experiment may be seriously biased as a consequence of the assignment of subjects to conditions.

It is also possible that the differences among children treated alike are due wholly or in part to errors of measurement. If the children do not really differ from one another, and if the measurement process is so crude or defective as to produce such varied scores within a group, then it is entirely possible that the differences between the two conditions are due to errors of measurement. Errors may have accumulated in one group, thereby favoring that group over the other.

We may wonder, too, about other influences beyond the control of the experimenter. Suppose a distracting event occurred while one group was scoring papers causing several children in that group to make errors in their scoring. The negative cheating scores come to mind at once as possibly due to scoring errors. The apparent difference between the groups may be explainable in terms of simple mistakes in counting, resulting from the distraction. Other possible sources of error or bias would soon occur to us if we continued to reflect on the experiment and, especially so, if we had before us an accurate and complete description of the experimental procedure.

The issues which have been mentioned as complicating the interpretation of experimental results are nothing new; they have been on the research scene for a long time. Psychologists not only acknowledge the presence of error in their observations and bias in their experiments but accept their presence as inevitable. This acceptance of error and bias as unavoidable implies that we cannot rely upon a single experiment for the demonstration of a natural phenomenon, that we can never interpret the results of research, even when it is repeated, with absolute certainty, and that our knowledge of any phenomenon is always tentative and partial, never final and complete.

A SOLUTION TO THE PROBLEM OF EVALUATION

Although his observations always contain errors and his research is always subject to bias, the experimenter does have recourse to methods which make it possible to evaluate his results. Developments which have taken place in the theory of statistical inference since the turn of the century provide the basis for a carefully reasoned, systematic procedure for making a decision as to the outcome of an experiment. When an experiment can be represented by a statistical model, the model makes possible a logically satisfying and conventionally accepted method of evaluation. Statistical models have been found to be of great practical value in the evaluation of research in several fields of study, the most prominent of which is probably agriculture.

We should hasten to add that evaluation employing statistical inference is not without its difficulties. The current widespread use of statistics is accompanied, as everyone knows and acknowledges, by what can only be described as flagrant abuses. It will be our purpose throughout the ensuing discussion to make explicit the circumstances under which legitimate and satisfactory applications of statistical inference can be made in experimental research.

If one keeps in mind at all times that a statistical model is a general, abstract, symbolic representation of an experiment, he is less likely to misuse it than if he does not, for the question of the correspondence between the characteristics of the model and the characteristics of the experiment will not as often be overlooked. When the model does correspond to the actual experiment, it can be used by the investigator to reach a decision that he can trust and defend. This is not to say that he will, in every instance, make a correct decision as to the outcome of an experiment. Disappointing as it may be to the student who is being introduced to statistical inference, we can make no claim for the infallibility of the experimenter, using even the most elegant of statistical procedures. Odd as it may appear to the student, the rigor of the evaluation inheres in another aspect of the process. The experimenter's decision that he has positive results in a particular instance may be incorrect, but the relative frequency or probability of his making such an erroneous decision in a very large number of experiments can be stated. Therein lies the rigor of the method. When the properties of the statistical model do not correspond to the properties of the experiment, the uncritical use of the model in evaluating results leads to decisions whose probability of being erroneous cannot be specified.

We shall see that the appropriate use of a statistical model in making a decision about the results of an experiment presupposes the fulfillment of certain requirements with respect to the correspondence between the model and the experimental situation. Meeting the requirements for the use of a statistic is a task which always challenges and frequently frustrates the ingenuity of the experimenter. Indeed, he can seldom, if ever, expect to fulfill these requirements exactly. Since, in most cases, he must accept an approximate fulfillment of the requirements, he should so plan, conduct, evaluate, and report his investigation as to establish and justify his own confidence, and the confidence of his colleagues, in his work.

PREVIEW

The problems of planning and conducting an experiment to meet the requirements of a meaningful, statistical interpretation are the problems of experimental design.   In general, a proper design should serve two functions: First, it should provide opportunity for the comparisons required by the hypotheses of the experimenter.   Second, it should enable the experimenter, in evaluating his data, to take account of the magnitude of errors to which the experiment is, in reality, liable.

In discussing the first function, that of providing the desired experimental comparisons, we shall consider a variety of plans for imposing treatments on subjects.   Initially, the treatment plan for a simple experiment having a single independent variable will be examined.   Later, the logic of the comparisons involved in the more comprehensive treatment plans for experiments having more than one independent variable will be presented.   These comprehensive treatment plans are often referred to as *factorial designs*.   Finally, we shall consider certain specific experimental comparisons that, when they are properly chosen or constructed, provide important information about the nature of the function for the relation between dependent and independent variables.

Evaluation, the second function served by a design, is accomplished by means of statistical tests of significance.   A detailed account of the rationale of tests of significance will be included with the early discussion of simple experiments involving a single independent variable.   At the same time, the basic statistical methods for handling the variability of observations will be reviewed.   Consideration will also be given to two topics of the greatest importance to an understanding of sound experimentation.   The two topics are "validity" and "precision", and the conditions of which they are a function will demand our attention repeatedly.   We shall see that the issues of validity and precision arise in connection with (a) the selection of subjects and their assignment to treatments and (b) the management of irrelevant influences in the course of the experimentation.

REFERENCE

1. Gach, H., "The Effect Upon Cheating of Varying Verbal Instructions," Unpublished master's thesis, Pennsylvania State University, 1955.

THE SINGLE-VARIABLE
EXPERIMENT

3

The classic, reference design is the single-variable experiment in which one independent variable is manipulated. The simplest form of the single-variable experiment requires two conditions or treatments. These conditions are imposed on a selection of experimental materials that, in a psychological experiment, will be human or animal subjects. After the conditions are imposed on these subjects, measurements are made on a response variable.

The act of assigning subjects to treatments is a critical point in the conduct of an experiment. No matter how it is done, the possibility of biasing the experimental comparison remains. The problem is not exactly the same in every experimental situation, but certain general principles can be stated that, if they are followed, place a psychological experiment on a sound footing. These principles will be discussed below.

THE ADVANTAGE OF SEPARATE GROUPS

In Chapter 2, no explanation was given for the suggestion that subjects be assigned to two groups corresponding to the two treatments, in which case no subject would receive more than one treatment or be measured more than once on the dependent variable. It is sometimes possible and, as will be seen later, desirable to use the same subjects in both conditions. In using the same subjects twice we impose one treatment on them, measure their responses, impose a different treatment on the same individuals, and obtain a second measure. Measures for the two treatments, having been obtained on the same group of subjects, are then compared to provide an evaluation of the

15

experiment. While the repeated use of the same subjects is sometimes feasible, it is often open to serious criticism.

Frequently, in research on living organisms, a single instance of treatment and measurement spoils subjects for any further use in that research Either the imposition of a treatment or the measurement of a response, or the combination, produces a change in the individual subject that endures and affects the results of additional treatment and measurement. The change is sometimes one that makes it impossible or absurd to impose a second treatment and obtain a second measure. In animal research, for example, the organism may have been physically sacrificed on the first occasion, as when examination and measurement of an internal organ is carried out. In research on humans, it would be ill-advised to apply successively to the same subjects, for purposes of comparison, two extended courses of psychotherapy of different kinds, or two methods of teaching the solution to a problem in mathematics. In the first case, the clients might be "cured" by the initial course of therapy. In the second case, the subjects might "know" how to solve the problem after the initial method of instruction was employed. In these two examples, the implication is that no further change is possible after the first treatment. Even when further change is possible, it may be limited and a biased comparison may result.

When two treatments are applied to the same subjects, the bias, if there is one, may depend on the order of imposing the treatments. Treatments actually having different effects may appear to have the same one. Treatments actually having the same effects may appear to have different ones. As an example, let us suppose that the effects of the two treatments, A and B, are actually different and that A is always imposed first and B second. Let us suppose further that A permanently improves the performance of the subjects and that B has no effect. When B is imposed on the same subjects, it will produce no additional improvement in performance, but will appear to be as effective as A when, in reality, it is not. B will appear to have the same effect as A simply because it has been applied to changed organisms. The observed difference is not between A and B, but rather between A and B-imposed-after-A. Other possibilities of bias arising from the order of imposing treatments may occur to the student.

It is not impossible to design a proper experiment employing repeated treatment and measurement when the changes are relatively enduring ones, but such designs are often quite complicated and are sometimes unnecessary. Counterbalancing or varying the orders of imposing treatments, and classifying the observations according to somewhat complex schemes for purposes of analysis are techniques frequently used. It is true that, in some cases, the change produced by an initial treatment and measurement is of only momentary duration. In these cases, the same subjects can be used repeatedly without bias to the comparison. Although repeated treatment and measurement is sometimes possible and desirable, discussion of such designs will be deferred until certain basic issues have been considered in connection with the use of a separate group of subjects for each condition in the experiment, a practice of more general interest and applicability.

THE ADVANTAGE OF REPLICATION

In Chapter 2, no reason was given for assigning a number of subjects to a particular treatment. Why not use just one subject in each condition? To answer this question, let us suppose that we have chosen a response variable and two conditions for investigation. We are interested in knowing whether or not these two conditions will have different effects on the response in question.

If we use only one subject in each condition, then we shall need only two for the experiment. One condition can be imposed on the first subject; the other condition can be imposed on the second. Let A and B represent the two conditions and S_1 and S_2 be the two subjects arbitrarily assigned to the conditions. The treatment plan can then be symbolized as

$$
\begin{array}{cc}
A & B \\
\hline
S_1 & S_2 \\
\hline
\end{array}
$$

Two measures can be obtained, one on each of the two individuals, and a comparison can be made of these two measures. Suppose that the two measures are 56 and 46 for S_1 and S_2, respectively. They could be recorded as

$$
\begin{array}{cc}
A & B \\
\hline
56 & 46 \\
\hline
\end{array}
$$

We observe a difference of $(56 - 46) = 10$ units between the two measures.

It is impossible to evaluate the observed difference of ten units. What assurance do we have that the two subjects were identical with respect to their responses before the different treatments were applied? The answer is, none. There is no way of guaranteeing that the two individuals selected for the experiment provided opportunity for an exact, errorless comparison.

Any initial difference between the two with respect to the response being measured would constitute an error in the comparison.

If the experimenter had perfectly homogeneous materials available, that is, subjects who were identical with respect to the characteristic of response being investigated and if there were no other sources of error, then the use of two subjects, one in each condition, would be quite appropriate. No error would be introduced into the comparison by a pre-experimental difference between individuals. Unfortunately, evidence of perfect homogeneity of humans or animals is not to be found. Psychologists know that the difference between two subjects with respect to a measure of a given response may be very large indeed. Small or large, any such difference will act to reduce or increase the apparent effect of one treatment relative to the other. When the experimenter uses only one subject for each condition, he has only one difference to evaluate and it contains both treatment effect and error. Given only one difference, he has no way of knowing either the magnitude of the error or the direction of influence which the error has exerted on the difference produced by the treatments.

The heterogeneity of experimental materials, that is, the pre-experimental differences among subjects, constitutes a major source of errors to which psychological experiments are liable. In due time other sources of errors will be discussed. Let us consider, at this point, how the experimenter, in evaluating the results of an experiment, can take account of the bias produced by differences among subjects.

Let us focus first upon the advantage of *replication*, by which we mean having more than one subject in each of the two conditions. If four subjects, S_1, S_2, S_3, and S_4, are arbitrarily assigned to the two conditions, A and B, the plan of treatment might be

A	B
S_1	S_2
S_3	S_4

Imagine that the four measures obtained are those given below

A	B
56	46
48	50

The average response for condition A is $(56 + 48)/2 = 52$; for B it is $(46 + 50)/2 = 48$. The difference between means is four units, in favor of A. Is this apparent difference in favor of A real, or is it only a difference produced by the assignment of subjects? We note that individuals treated alike differ. The difference for those under condition A is $(56 - 48) = 8$ units; the difference under condition B is $(50 - 46) = 4$ units. If subjects treated alike differ so much, is it not possible that the difference between means is a consequence of the way individuals happened to be assigned and not a consequence of treatment? The difference between the two conditions is not impressive, considering the heterogeneity of the subjects and the fact that they were arbitrarily assigned to the conditions. When we are doing research with subjects as heterogeneous as these, we can reasonably expect that the comparison of A and B will sometimes be biased by several units or more.

Imagine another possible outcome of an experiment as indicated in the following tabulation

A	B
52	73
54	71

The mean for A is 53. The mean for B is 72. The difference between means is $(72 - 53) = 19$ units. The apparent difference is in favor of B. Is it due to treatment or due to the assignment of subjects? We note that subjects treated alike, in each condition, differ by only two units. They are so homogeneous that we would not expect to obtain a difference between means of 19 units just by assigning them to the two groups. We could be fairly confident that conditions A and B actually have different effects on responses.

The advantage of replication should now be apparent. The experimental comparison requires observations on individuals treated differently. Introducing replication insures that we have observations on individuals treated alike. The variability of observations obtained under the same condition tells us about the magnitude of the differences among our subjects, which differences are potential errors or biases. Thus it is often said that replication provides an estimate of error.*

* To simplify this early discussion, we have considered only errors arising from the selection of subjects and their assignment to treatments. Other sources of error will be introduced later. The benefits of replication in estimating error apply to these other sources as well.

Evaluation of the experiment logically involves comparing differences among subjects treated differently with differences among subjects treated alike. In other words, the apparent effects of treatment must be compared to an estimate of the magnitude of errors affecting the experiment. When treatment differences are large relative to subject differences, we are inclined to accept the treatment differences as real. When they are not, we are inclined to view them as the result of biasing errors.

A DEFECT

Our reasoning has a flaw. The arbitrary assignment can itself lead us astray in a fashion we have not yet considered.

Imagine that we had four subjects, S_1, S_2, S_3, and S_4. Imagine, too, that S_1 and S_2 were comparable, that S_3 and S_4 were comparable, but that S_1 and S_2 were quite different from S_3 and S_4. Then the assignment

$$
\begin{array}{cc}
A & B \\
\hline
\begin{matrix} S_1 \\ S_2 \end{matrix} & \begin{matrix} S_3 \\ S_4 \end{matrix} \\
\end{array}
$$

would produce a large bias in the experimental comparison and an underestimate of that bias. Differences between subjects treated alike would be much smaller than the bias affecting the experiment. On the other hand, the arrangement

$$
\begin{array}{cc}
A & B \\
\hline
\begin{matrix} S_1 \\ S_3 \end{matrix} & \begin{matrix} S_2 \\ S_4 \end{matrix} \\
\end{array}
$$

would result in a small bias in the experimental comparison and an overestimate of that bias. Differences among subjects treated alike would be much larger than the bias affecting the experiment.

Thus we must admit that, simply as a consequence of the assignment, the actual bias can be large or small relative to the estimate of it. The objectionable feature of the system of evaluation is that, when the actual bias is large relative to the estimate, we will mistakenly conclude that the treatment differences are real. The system of evaluation will somehow have to take account of those outcomes which appear to be most favorable but which are actually due to error.

THE DEFECT REMEDIED

The occurrence of these misleading outcomes cannot be prevented. As long as experiments are liable to errors, the possibility remains that these errors will combine in a way that will prompt the experimenter to conclude, mistakenly, that he has positive results. Although the experimenter cannot avoid being misled, except by interpreting all results as due to error, he can fix the percentage or proportion of his decisions that will be erroneous and he can make that percentage as small as he wants it to be.

For any given experiment, there are usually many different ways in which errors can combine to affect the results. Under certain circumstances, which will be discussed in detail later, it is possible to specify these many error outcomes. In the totality of such events varying degrees of what might be called *favorableness* for an interpretation of positive results will be represented. Those outcomes with the largest apparent treatment effects and the smallest estimate of errors will be the most favorable. Those outcomes with the smallest apparent treatment effects and the largest estimate of errors will be the least favorable. Since he has to risk being misled by error, it seems only reasonable that the experimenter should take his chances on the most favorable outcomes. At the same time, he will certainly want to limit the relative frequency of his mistakes. He can do so by establishing a class of the most favorable outcomes, about which he is willing to be mistaken, and he can make the size of the class small relative to the totality of events.

Mathematical statistics plays an important role in the solving of the experimenter's evaluation problem. It is a fundamental exercise in mathematical statistics to determine by deduction what are all of the possible error outcomes of an experiment. Once the totality of error outcomes has been established, it is a simple matter to set the size of the class of the most favorable events, which events are to be interpreted as evidence of positive results.

RANDOM ASSIGNMENT AND BIAS

Up to this point we have spoken of the arbitrary assignment of subjects to conditions. The method of assignment deserves further discussion. Consider the dilemma of the experimenter. He has available a supply of subjects from which he must select some number for experimentation. He must divide the selected individuals into two groups. The two groups will be treated differently and then compared. He must admit that he cannot select subjects and constitute the two groups so that he can be sure no bias will enter the experimental comparison. The subjects are undoubtedly hetero-geneous in their responses. Furthermore, since he does not possess errorless methods of measurement, he cannot determine the exact degree of hetero-geneity and, therefore, cannot match the two groups so that they are exactly comparable at the start of the experiment.

He realizes that he must avoid any method of assigning individuals that would be influenced directly or indirectly by his own personal judgment. To use such a method would make him vulnerable to the accusation that subjects were assigned to favor his hypotheses. There is obvious need for what might be termed a *mechanical* system which would operate independently of his judgment in assigning subjects.

It is not sufficient, however, to require only that the mechanical system of assigning be independent of the personal judgment of the experimenter. It is also important that the system be independent of the responses of the subjects. A system would not be satisfactory if, in placing individuals, it tended to select high scorers on the dependent variable for condition A and low scorers for condition B. Such a system would be as objectionable as the bias of the experimenter's personal judgment.

Evidently what is needed is a mechanical system like the tossing of a coin, the throwing of a die, or the drawing of lots—a system which would make assignments independently of the experimenter's judgment and the charac-teristics of the respondents. It is true that such a system would not eliminate bias in any given experiment. Our experience with coins, dice, and lotteries provides us with a fairly good idea of the way in which the bias would be distributed, but we would expect that errors accompanying the assigning of subjects to treatments would tend to cancel one another. We would also expect this canceling of errors to be more complete and occur more often with larger numbers of subjects than with smaller numbers. In a long series of experiments, the system would bias the comparison in favor of A as often as it would do so in favor of B. A large accumulated bias in either direction would occur relatively infrequently. Small biases would occur more often than larger ones.

The student may react at this point with little enthusiasm for a system of assigning subjects that still produces a bias of unknown magnitude and direction, even if the system is independent of the experimenter's judgment and subjects' responses. It is certainly true that the possibility of bias and the consequent uncertainty of interpretation are not removed. It remains to be seen just why the mechanical system is preferred over any other.

The additional advantage of a mechanical system such as the tossing of a coin, the throwing of a die, or the drawing of lots is that its results can be deduced or predicted. That is to say, it can be demonstrated empirically that the outcomes of mechanically assigning subjects approximate quite closely the outcomes formally deduced from probability theory in mathematical statistics. We can make good use of the correspondence between the concept of random or chance error, as it is defined in probability theory, and the mechanical assigning of subjects by coin, die, or lot. It is conventional to refer to mechanical assignment as *random* assignment and, since the empirical outcome approximates the theoretical outcome, it is not inappropriate to do so.

In randomly assigning subjects, a number of different outcomes are possible. Sometimes the number is very large. By an application of probability theory one can deduce the nature of all outcomes. In a real experiment, of course, the actual presence or absence—or amount—of treatment effect will not be known. Outcomes of chance alone will not be distinguishable from outcomes embodying real treatment effects. Consequently, we shall have to risk mistaking chance effects for real treatment effects. Since we know what all the chance outcomes are, we can specify those we are willing to mistake for real ones.

THE STATISTICAL TEST OF SIGNIFICANCE

The point was developed earlier that, in order to take account of the bias resulting from the assigning of heterogeneous subjects to experimental conditions, the differences in response between groups treated differently should be compared to the differences in response between subjects treated alike. We have also seen that random assignment makes it possible to fix and specify the number of chance outcomes to be mistaken for real effects. A test of significance serves both of these purposes. It embodies a comparison of the difference between conditions with differences among subjects. It makes possible the specification of the relative number of erroneous decisions in which outcomes due to error are interpreted as real effects.

We should emphasize that the evaluation cannot be said to be rigorous in the sense that it is always correct. It *can* be said to be rigorous in the sense that the experimenter can fix in advance the probability that he will make an erroneous decision. In using a test of significance, it is the choice of a *level of significance* that fixes the relative number of chance outcomes he is willing to interpret mistakenly as real effects.

One thing more should be said about mechanical systems of assigning subjects. Any assurance that a system has the properties it should have can only be based upon the actual testing of the system to see whether or not it will approximate the theoretical model. Dice, coins, and lotteries are not used as frequently at the present time as they once were because of the labor involved in testing them. Much more convenient for present use are the so-called *tables of random numbers*, several of which are readily available and have been tested. Suggestions for the use of these tables will be made at a later time.

SUMMARY

We have described how experiments are biased by the assignment of subjects to treatments. We have presented the reasoning which recommends random or chance methods of assignment. We must next indicate how statistical inference, in the form of tests of significance, can accomplish for the experimenter a standard and objective comparison and evaluation of the kind suggested by our common-sense approach to the problem.

PREVIEW

An understanding of the use of a test of significance requires a considerable background of information. To insure that the student will have the necessary background, those basic elements of statistics having to do with the handling of quantitative variation will be reviewed in Chapter 4. In this connection, the use of certain statistical symbolism will be explained. In Chapter 5 a brief discussion of sampling variability and probability statements will be undertaken. We will then be in a position to take up, in Chapter 6, the formal design and evaluation of the single-variable experiment.

The formal evaluation of an experiment can be conceived of as resting upon four basic propositions, around which the presentation of the next three chapters will be organized:

1. Variability, the differences in a set of quantitative observations, can be measured and analyzed into components.

2. Components of variability can be compared and the sampling outcomes of these comparisons can be deduced.

3. In a true experiment, at least two components of variability can be isolated and identified. The one component represents the differences which are apparently due to the effects of the treatments but which, in fact, may be due to errors, the effects of treatments, or the combined effects of

both. The other source provides information concerning the magnitude of the errors to which the experiment is liable.

4. The apparent treatment differences in an experiment are suspect but can be evaluated. The treatment differences can be compared to the errors, a circumstance which provides the basis for making a decision as to the success of the experiment.

BASIC STATISTICS

4

The experimenter, when he examines his data, is confronted with variability. Some contribution to the observed differences may have come from the different effects of the treatments. Some contribution has undoubtedly come from errors. Seldom does the experimenter find that he can, on the basis of an inspection of the data, reach a decision as to the outcome of the experiment. Fortunately, the differences can be examined and dealt with by standard and objective methods which considerably reduce the complexity and uncertainty which attends an inspectional judgment.

We shall review briefly three ways of measuring variability, which the student should remember from his first work in descriptive statistics. They are the sum of squares of deviations from the mean, the variance, and the standard deviation. In measuring variability in a group of observations, the mean is taken as a reference point and the deviation of an observation from the mean can be thought of as the contribution of that observation to the variability. The sum of squares of the deviations from the mean is a value which reflects the magnitude of the differences among the observations. The sum of squared deviations is thus useful as an index of the variability in a collection of measures. The average of these squared deviations is called the *variance* or sometimes the *mean square*. The square root of the variance is the familiar *standard deviation*.

THE SYMBOLISM OF SUMS

Sums of varied kinds recur constantly in statistics. There is a convenient and efficient method of expressing the summing operation symbolically and a brief consideration of its use will facilitate communication from this point on.

The Greek capital letter Σ or *sigma* indicates a summation.

Thus,

$$Y_1 + Y_2 + Y_3 + \cdots + Y_n$$

can be written as

$$\Sigma Y$$

and read as "the sum of the n values of Y." Other common expressions involving sigma are given below, with their definitions.

$\Sigma X = X_1 + X_2 + X_3 + \cdots + X_n =$ the sum of the n values of X.

$(\Sigma Y)^2 = (Y_1 + Y_2 + Y_3 + \cdots + Y_n)^2 =$ the square of the sum of the n values of Y.

$\Sigma Y^2 = Y_1^2 + Y_2^2 + Y_3^2 + \cdots + Y_n^2 =$ the sum of the squares of the values of Y.

$\Sigma(X + Y) = (X_1 + Y_1) + (X_2 + Y_2) + (X_3 + Y_3) + \cdots + (X_n + Y_n) =$ the sum of the sums, $(X + Y)$. Note the pairing of X and Y values implied by the subscripts.

$\Sigma XY = X_1Y_1 + X_2Y_2 + X_3Y_3 + \cdots + X_nY_n =$ the sum of the products, XY. Note again the pairing implied by the subscripts.

$\Sigma(X/Y) = X_1/Y_1 + X_2/Y_2 + X_3/Y_3 + \cdots + X_n/Y_n =$ the sum of the quotients, X/Y.

$(\Sigma X)(\Sigma Y) = (X_1 + X_2 + X_3 + \cdots + X_n)(Y_1 + Y_2 + Y_3 + \cdots + Y_n) =$ the product of the sum of X and the sum of Y.

The student would do well to familiarize himself with the use of sigma. Note that it is not a number; rather, it indicates an operation to be performed. The operation is that of summing. If one considers the operation completed, then ΣY and the other expressions involving the sign and listed above represent numbers and can be treated as numerical quantities.

To avoid confusion in writing more complex expressions, "limits" and "indices" must be employed. Limits are written above and below the summation. The lower limit indicates the first term in the summation. The upper limit gives the last term. The summation is always defined as covering all terms embraced by the limits. For example, in

$$\sum_{i=1}^{n} X_i$$

the expression $i = 1$ is the lower limit, indicating that X_1 is the first term in the summation; n is the upper limit indicating that X_n is the last term.

Indices are used to identify and classify the values. Suppose the N values of X are classified into c subsets with n values in each subset. We may use the indices i and k as subscripts to denote any value in any subset. That is, X_{ik} is read as "the ith value in the kth subset." Numerical subscripts would indicate a particular value in a particular subset. Thus X_{42} would refer to the fourth value in the second subset.

The sum for any subset would be written as

$$\sum_{i=1}^{n} X_{ik}.$$

The sum of the subset sums would be

$$\sum_{k=1}^{c} \sum_{i=1}^{n} X_{ik},$$

which is defined as

$$\sum_{i=1}^{n} X_{i1} + \sum_{i=1}^{n} X_{i2} + \sum_{i=1}^{n} X_{i3} + \cdots + \sum_{i=1}^{n} X_{ic}.$$

It happens that in our usage the lower limit will always be "1", so that the symbolism can be simplified somewhat. The sum of the subset sums could be written as

$$\sum_{k}^{c} \sum_{i}^{n} X_{ik}.$$

The sum of the subset sums is the same as the sum of all N values.

Whenever possible, we shall avoid the use of limits and indices and adopt the simplest symbolism consonant with clear expression. It may be possible to do so at times when the verbal context serves to qualify the summing operation. There will be times, however, when clear expression will necessitate the use of limits and indices.

The mean and the three measures of variability can be conveniently defined by expressions involving the summation sign. The mean of Y is given by $\Sigma Y / n$, where n is the number of values in the summation. The symbol $\bar{Y}$ will be used to represent the mean. The formula for the mean can thus be written as

$$\bar{Y} = \frac{\Sigma Y}{n}.$$

The difference between any value and the mean is sometimes represented by the small letter, y. That is,

$$y = Y - \bar{Y}.$$

The sum of squares of deviations from the mean is then

$$\Sigma y^2.$$

The average of the squared deviations, or the variance, V_y, is

$$\frac{\Sigma y^2}{n}.$$

The standard deviation, S_y, is the square root of the variance as indicated by

$$\sqrt{\frac{\Sigma y^2}{n}}.$$

RULES OF SUMMATION

Computation is often facilitated by certain changes or *simplifications* that can be made in expressions involving the summation sign. The changes are not difficult to perform if one observes four rules.

The first rule can be stated as follows: When Σ is written before an expression involving two or more terms, it can be rewritten before each term in the expression. Here is an example. The expression

$$\Sigma(X + Y)$$

can be rewritten

$$\Sigma X + \Sigma Y.$$

By definition, $(X + Y)$ means that each X value is paired with a Y value and the members of each pair are to be added. Writing $\Sigma(X + Y)$ implies that the pair sums are to be added. Since the order of addition does not affect the sum, we would obtain exactly the same answer by adding the X values, adding the Y values, and combining the two sums—a set of operations indicated by the expression $\Sigma X + \Sigma Y$.

Another application of the first rule is the following:

$$\Sigma(X + Y + Z) = \Sigma X + \Sigma Y + \Sigma Z.$$

The second rule involves the notion of a constant value. When Σ is written before the product of a constant and a variable, the expression can be rewritten with the constant before Σ. Let a be a constant and Y, a variable. Then, according to the rule,

$$\Sigma a Y$$

can be rewritten as

$$a \Sigma Y$$

By definition, $\Sigma a Y$ means that each Y value is to be multiplied by the constant and these products are to be summed. We would obtain the same answer by summing the Y values and multiplying the sum by the constant. That is,

$$\begin{aligned}
\Sigma a Y &= a Y_1 + a Y_2 + a Y_3 + \cdots + a Y_n \\
&= a(Y_1 + Y_2 + Y_3 + \cdots + Y_n) \\
&= a \Sigma Y.
\end{aligned}$$

Another application of the second rule is the following:

$$\Sigma 2a\,X = 2a\,\Sigma\,X.$$

The third rule for the use of the summation sign is that an expression in which Σ is written before a constant can be rewritten as a product of the constant and the number of terms in the summation. For example,

$$\Sigma a$$

can be rewritten as

$$na$$

when a is a constant and n is the number of terms in the summation. Σa is defined as the sum of n quantities each of which has the constant value a. The same definition applies to the product, na. The student may recall that multiplication is defined as repeated addition and see that, as a consequence, $\Sigma a = na$.

Applying the third rule to the expression

$$\Sigma 5a^2,$$

we may write

$$5a^2 n.$$

The fourth rule is that an expression in which Σ is written before the product (or quotient) of two variables cannot be simplified. For example, ΣXY cannot be rewritten. By definition, XY implies that each X value is paired with a Y value and the product of the members of each pair is to be obtained. Writing ΣXY indicates that these products are to be summed. That is,

$$\Sigma XY = X_1 Y_1 + X_2 Y_2 + X_3 Y_3 + \cdots + X_n Y_n,$$

which expression does not lend itself to any simplification.

COMPUTING FORMULAS

The simplification rules are useful in deriving computing formulas. For example, the quantity Σy^2, which is the sum of squares of deviations from the mean, would, in most cases, be troublesome to compute if we obtained and squared each deviation and then added the squares. Instead, we note that Σy^2 is defined as

$$\Sigma(Y - \bar{Y})^2,$$

which can be thought of as a sum of products of two variables. By reference to the fourth rule, we see that a sum of products of variable quantities cannot be rewritten. If we carry out the indicated squaring, however, we obtain

$$\Sigma(Y^2 - 2\bar{Y}Y + \bar{Y}^2),$$

which can be rewritten, by application of the first rule, to yield

$$\Sigma Y^2 - \Sigma 2\bar{Y}Y + \Sigma\bar{Y}^2.$$

The second rule can now be applied to the second term and the third rule to the third term, yielding

$$\Sigma Y^2 - 2\bar{Y}\Sigma Y + n\bar{Y}^2.$$

Recall that $\bar{Y} = \Sigma Y/n$, which can be substituted in the preceding expression, giving

$$\Sigma Y^2 - \frac{2(\Sigma Y)^2}{n} + \frac{n(\Sigma Y)^2}{n^2}$$

or

$$\Sigma Y^2 - \frac{2(\Sigma Y)^2}{n} + \frac{(\Sigma Y)^2}{n}.$$

Combining the second and third terms yields a convenient computing formula:

$$\Sigma Y^2 - \frac{(\Sigma Y)^2}{n}. \tag{4.1}$$

The sum of squares of deviations from the mean can thus be computed by finding ΣY and ΣY^2, the sum and the sum of squares of the original measures. Both summations can be performed very efficiently on an automatic desk calculator.

It will be well to establish, at this point, a preference in the use of certain words. Both Σy^2 and ΣY^2 are sums of squares. Σy^2 refers to deviations; ΣY^2 refers to the original measures. We shall want to refer more frequently to Σy^2 than to ΣY^2. Therefore, we shall reserve the term "sum of squares" without qualification for Σy^2. For ΣY^2 we shall use the expression, "sum of squares of original measures."

The review of basic statistics has thus far covered certain values used to measure variability, the symbolism employed to represent these values, and the derivation of a computing formula. It will be appropriate next to examine methods of analyzing the variability in measures classified into groups.

THE ANALYSIS OF VARIABILITY

Ten hypothetical measures have been classified, in Table 4.1, into two columns, labeled I and II, of five numbers each.

Table 4.1

TEN HYPOTHETICAL MEASURES
CLASSIFIED INTO TWO SUBSETS

I	II
3	9
1	5
5	6
4	8
2	7

The mean of the ten numbers is 5. Disregarding the classification for the moment, we find that the total variability in the entire set, as measured by the sum of squares,* is 60.

The variability in each column can be measured in a similar fashion. The mean of column I is 3; the sum of squares is 10. The mean of column II is 7; the sum of squares is 10. Combining these two sums of squares yields a measure of the variability within the columns. Thus $(10 + 10) = 20$. This quantity is often referred to as the *within-column sum of squares*, a measure of the variability within the columns.

Let us now eliminate the variability in each column by substituting the mean of the column for each number in that column.

The values resulting from the substitution are shown in Table 4.2. Notice that the variability within each column has now been eliminated but that

Table 4.2

THE HYPOTHETICAL MEASURES OF TABLE 4.1 AFTER
ELIMINATION OF WITHIN-COLUMN VARIABILITY

I	II
3	7
3	7
3	7
3	7
3	7

* Remember that *sum of squares* means sum of squared deviations.

some variability does remain in the entire set. It is convenient and obviously appropriate to describe this remaining variability as differences between columns or as *between-column* variability.

Eliminating variability within the columns has not changed the mean of the entire set. It is still 5. The sum of squares for the entire set is now 40. That is to say, the between-column variability, as measured by the sum of squares, is 40.

In the example we observe the following interesting relation:

$$\begin{array}{lll} \text{Total} & = \text{Between-column} + \text{Within-column} \\ \text{variability} & \text{variability} & \text{variability} \end{array}$$

In numerical terms, the relation is

$$60 = 40 + (10 + 10)$$
$$60 = 40 + 20.$$

It can be seen that the total variability has been analyzed into two components, differences between columns and differences within columns.

In presenting the numerical example above, the generality of the method of analysis has not been established. We can do so by employing the symbolism and rules of simplification discussed earlier.

Let c = the number of columns,
n = the number of values in each column,
$N = nc$ = the total number of values,
Y_{ik} = the ith value in the kth column,
$\bar{Y}_{.k}$ = the mean of the kth column,
$\bar{Y}_{..}$ = the mean of all N values.

The demonstration begins with the following identity:

$$Y_{ik} - \bar{Y}_{..} = (Y_{ik} - \bar{Y}_{.k}) + (\bar{Y}_{.k} - \bar{Y}_{..}).$$

The identity can be stated in words as follows: The deviation of a measure from the total mean can be expressed as consisting of two additive parts, the deviation of the value from its column mean and the deviation of that column mean from the total mean. The equality is undeniably satisfied, since the combining of terms in the right member would make it identical with the left member.

Squaring both members of the identity, we obtain

$$(Y_{ik} - \bar{Y}_{..})^2 = (Y_{ik} - \bar{Y}_{.k})^2 + 2(Y_{ik} - \bar{Y}_{.k})(\bar{Y}_{.k} - \bar{Y}_{..}) + (\bar{Y}_{.k} - \bar{Y}_{..})^2.$$

Summing within a single column over n terms gives, in the left member,

$$\Sigma(Y_{ik} - \bar{Y}_{..})^2$$

and, in the right member,

$$(\quad \Sigma[(Y_{ik} - \bar{Y}_{.k})^2 + 2(Y_{ik} - \bar{Y}_{.k})(\bar{Y}_{.k} - \bar{Y}_{..}) + (\bar{Y}_{.k} - \bar{Y}_{..})^2].$$

The first simplification rule may be applied to the right member of the equation, yielding

$$\Sigma(Y_{ik} - \bar{Y}_{.k})^2 + \Sigma 2(Y_{ik} - \bar{Y}_{.k})(\bar{Y}_{.k} - \bar{Y}_{..}) + \Sigma(\bar{Y}_{.k} - \bar{Y}_{..})^2.$$

In the second term, "2" is a constant and $(\bar{Y}_{.k} - \bar{Y}_{..})$ is constant for any given column. Applying the second rule gives

$$\Sigma(Y_{ik} - \bar{Y}_{.k})^2 + 2(\bar{Y}_{.k} - \bar{Y}_{..})\Sigma(Y_{ik} - \bar{Y}_{.k}) + \Sigma(\bar{Y}_{.k} - \bar{Y}_{..})^2.$$

Examine $\Sigma(Y_{ik} - \bar{Y}_{.k})$, a factor in the second term. By the first rule of simplification, $\Sigma(Y_{ik} - \bar{Y}_{.k}) = \Sigma Y_{ik} - \Sigma \bar{Y}_{.k}$. Since there are n terms in the summation and $\bar{Y}_{.k}$ is a constant, $\Sigma Y_{ik} - \Sigma \bar{Y}_{.k} = \Sigma Y_{ik} - n\bar{Y}_{.k}$. Substituting $\Sigma Y_{ik}/n$ for $\bar{Y}_{.k}$ yields $\Sigma Y_{ik} - n\Sigma Y_{ik}/n = \Sigma Y_{ik} - \Sigma Y_{ik} = 0$, from which we see that the sum of deviations from the mean, for a given column, is zero. The second term on the right of the equation thus drops out, and the entire equation is

$$\Sigma(Y_{ik} - \bar{Y}_{..})^2 = \Sigma(Y_{ik} - \bar{Y}_{.k})^2 + \Sigma(\bar{Y}_{.k} - \bar{Y}_{..})^2.$$

Since $(\bar{Y}_{.k} - \bar{Y}_{..})^2$ is a constant, we may apply the third rule to the second term on the right and obtain

$$\Sigma(Y_{ik} - \bar{Y}_{..})^2 = \Sigma(Y_{ik} - \bar{Y}_{.k})^2 + n(\bar{Y}_{.k} - \bar{Y}_{..})^2,$$

which equation holds for any single column. Summing these quantities for any number of columns, c, requires the use of a double summation. Summing on the left and the right of the equation over c columns gives

$$\sum_k \sum_i (Y_{ik} - \bar{Y}_{..})^2 = \sum_k \sum_i (Y_{ik} - \bar{Y}_{.k})^2 + \sum_k n(\bar{Y}_{.k} - \bar{Y}_{..})^2$$

The lower limit is understood to be 1 in each instance. Where the index of summation is i, the upper limit is n; where the index of summation is k, the upper limit is c.

Examine the expression in the left member of the equation. It is the sum of the sums of squares of deviations from the total mean. Since a sum is not affected by the order of addition, this expression on the left is actually the total sum of squares of deviations from the mean, a measure of the total variability.

There are two terms in the right member of the equation. The first is the combined within-column sum of squares; the second represents what we have called the between-column variability.

The equation can be expressed in words as follows: The total sum of squares consists of two additive parts or components, the combined within-column sum of squares and the between-column sum of squares. The generality of the method of analysis for which a numerical example was given on page 33 has now been established.

COMPUTING FORMULAS

When numbers are classified into subsets, the total sum of squares is easily computed by disregarding the classification and applying formula (4.1) for the sum of squares of a single set of numbers. If we understand that the summation involves all N values in the entire set, then the formula can be modified and written

$$\Sigma Y^2 - \frac{(\Sigma Y)^2}{N}$$

or as
$$\Sigma Y^2 - C', \tag{4.2}$$

where C', the *correction term*, equals $(\Sigma Y)^2/N$, the square of the sum of the entire set of numbers divided by the number in the set.

The combined within-column sum of squares can be computed by starting with the same basic formula, (4.1). If we understand that the summation covers the n values in any column or subset, formula (4.1) for the sum of squares of any single column or subset can be written

$$\Sigma Y^2 - \frac{(\Sigma Y)^2}{n}.$$

The formula can be applied to each column in turn, producing a sum of squares for each. These sums of squares can be added to give the combined within-column sum of squares.

The between-column sum of squares has been defined as

$$\sum_k n(\bar{Y}_{.k} - \bar{Y}_{..})^2.$$

Consider the case in which n, the number of values in a column, is a constant. The constant can be written before the summation sign as follows:

$$n\sum_k (\bar{Y}_{.k} - \bar{Y}_{..})^2.$$

Squaring yields

$$n \sum_k (\bar{Y}_{.k}^2 - 2\bar{Y}_{.k}\bar{Y}_{..} + \bar{Y}_{..}^2).$$

Simplifying, we obtain

$$n\left(\sum_k \bar{Y}_{.k}^2 - 2\bar{Y}_{..} \sum_k \bar{Y}_{.k} + c\bar{Y}_{..}^2\right).$$

Substituting $\sum_i Y_{ik}/n$ for $\bar{Y}_{.k}$ produces

$$n\left[\frac{\sum_k \left(\sum_i Y_{ik}\right)^2}{n^2} - \frac{2\bar{Y}_{..} \sum_k \sum_i Y_{ik}}{n} + c\bar{Y}_{..}^2\right].$$

Multiplying by n yields

$$\frac{\sum_k \left(\sum_i Y_{ik}\right)^2}{n} - 2\bar{Y}_{..} \sum_k \sum_i Y_{ik} + nc\bar{Y}_{..}^2.$$

Nothing more can be done with the first term, but the second and third terms can be combined. $\bar{Y}_{..}$, the total mean, is equal to $\sum_k \sum_i Y_{ik}/nc$, the sum of the column sums divided by the total number of values. Substituting in the second term yields

$$-\frac{2\left(\sum_k \sum_i Y_{ik}\right)^2}{nc},$$

while substituting in the third term gives.

$$\frac{nc\left(\sum_k \sum_i Y_{ik}\right)^2}{n^2c^2}$$

or

$$\frac{\left(\sum_k \sum_i Y_{ik}\right)^2}{nc}.$$

Combining the second and third terms gives

$$-\frac{\left(\sum_k \sum_i Y_{ik}\right)^2}{nc},$$

which must be written together with the first term to give the complete computing formula

$$\frac{\sum_k \left(\sum_i Y_{ik}\right)^2}{n} - \frac{\left(\sum_k \sum_i Y_{ik}\right)^2}{nc},$$

which is equivalent to writing

$$\frac{\sum_k \left(\sum_i Y_{ik}\right)^2}{n} - C' \tag{4.3}$$

since
$$\frac{\left(\sum_k \sum_i Y_{ik}\right)^2}{nc}$$

is equal to C', as it was defined for formula (4.2).

In using the computing formula, (4.3), for the between-column sum of squares, we find the sum of each column, square each sum, add the squared sums and divide by n, the number of values in a column. The quotient obtained is the first term in the formula. The correction term, C', must then be subtracted from the first term.

AN EXAMPLE

The formulas derived above will now be applied to the classification of numbers given in Table 4.1.

The formula for the total sum of squares, (4.2), is

$$\Sigma Y^2 - C'$$

The summary data required are:

$$\Sigma Y = 50,$$
$$(\Sigma Y)^2 = 2500,$$
$$N = 10,$$
$$C' = (\Sigma Y)^2 / N = 2500/10 = 250,$$
$$\Sigma Y^2 = 310.$$

The computation of the total sum of squares:

$$310 - 250 = 60.$$

The formula for the within-column sum of squares for any column, formula (4.1), is

$$\Sigma Y^2 - \frac{(\Sigma Y)^2}{n}.$$

The summary data required for column I are:

$$\Sigma Y = 15,$$
$$(\Sigma Y)^2 = 225,$$
$$n = 5,$$
$$\Sigma Y^2 = 55.$$

Computation of the sum of squares for column I:

$$55 - 225/5 = 55 - 45 = 10.$$

The summary data required for column II are:

$$\Sigma Y = 35,$$
$$(\Sigma Y)^2 = 1225,$$
$$n = 5,$$
$$\Sigma Y^2 = 255.$$

Computation of the sum of squares for column II:

$$255 - 1225/5 = 255 - 245 = 10.$$

Combining the sums of squares for the two columns:

$$10 + 10 = 20.$$

The formula for the between-column sum of squares, formula (4.3):

$$\frac{\sum_k \left(\sum_i Y_{ik}\right)^2}{n} - C'.$$

The summary data required are:

$$\sum_i Y_{i1} = \text{the sum of column I} = 15,$$

$$\sum_i Y_{i2} = \text{the sum of column II} = 35,$$

$$\left(\sum_i Y_{i1}\right)^2 = 15^2 = 225,$$

$$\left(\sum_i Y_{i2}\right)^2 = 35^2 = 1225,$$

$$n = 5,$$
$$C' = 250.$$

Computation of the between-column sum of squares:

$$(225 + 1225)/5 - 250 = 1450/5 - 250 = 290 - 250 = 40.$$

When n, the number of values in each column, varies, one finds the sum of each column, squares each sum, divides each squared sum by the number of values in that column, and adds these quotients. The correction term is then subtracted.

The analysis of variability described above applies to any classification of numbers into columns or subsets. Other classifications of a more complex nature are also of interest to the experimenter and will be discussed later. All of these analyses are based on two fundamental notions: (a) variability can be measured in terms of sums of squares of deviations from means and (b) variability can be eliminated by substituting the appropriate mean for each of the values in a category.

SUMMARY

When numbers have been classified into subsets, the variability exhibited by the numbers can be analyzed into components. It is probably not difficult for the student to anticipate how the experimenter can make use of these methods of analysis. The variability exhibited by experimental data can be analyzed into treatment effects and error, components of very great interest to the investigator. How components of variability can be compared will be described in Chapter 5. How the comparisons can be employed in an evaluation of data from a single-variable experiment will be explained in Chapter 6.

RANDOM VARIATION

5

Components of random variability can be compared. The rationale upon which such comparisons are based is found in sampling theory. The meaningfulness and ultimate usefulness of these comparisons depend, in large part, on the correspondence between sampling theory and the operations of the experimenter as he attempts to implement it. Actually the common practices of the research psychologist only approximate the strict requirements of the theory. Exact correspondence is never knowingly achieved. Since the degree of correspondence is a critical matter, an attempt will be made to maintain a clear distinction between theory and practice by discussing them separately.

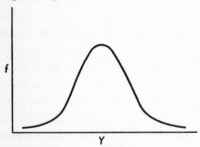

Fig. 5.1 A normal probability function or normal curve. The vertical scale or ordinate represents frequency. The horizontal scale or abscissa represents a variable, Y.

THEORY

Six elements of sampling theory will be briefly reviewed here. These elements involve the concepts of a universe or population of measures, random sampling, sampling variability, a sampling distribution, a frequency function, and a probability statement.

In theory, an assumption is made concerning the nature of the universe or population of measures. The assumption is that the population distribution is normal. That is to say, a normal probability function or normal curve is assumed to describe or to fit the population frequency distribution exactly. A normal probability function is a continuous curve with a characteristic shape or form (see Fig. 5.1). It is symmetrical, unimodal, and mesokurtic, that is, neither flat nor peaked. The branches approach but never reach the abscissa, no matter how far they are extended. Assuming that the population distribution is continuous implies that the population is indefinitely large. Values computed from the universe of measures are called *parameters*. Parameters are usually represented by Greek letters. For example, the population mean is represented by the letter μ. The population variance is indicated by σ^2, the square of the letter *sigma*.

According to theory, a sample can be selected from the population by random sampling, a method of selection that insures that each measure in the universe has an equal chance of being included and that the choice of any measure is independent of the choice of any other. A sample selected by this method is called a *random sample*. Values computed from a sample of measures are called *statistics*. Statistics are usually given letter symbols from the Latin alphabet.

One can deduce the results of random sampling. All of the possible values that a statistic can take, computed for a sample of given size, can be determined. These values exhibit variability. If they were arranged in a frequency distribution, that arrangement would be called a *sampling distribution*.

The sampling distribution of a given statistic has a characteristic form. In the case of certain statistics, the form of the sampling distribution of each is such that it can be described by one of several known mathematical functions. Certain characteristics of these frequency functions have been determined.

Knowing the sampling distribution of a statistic makes possible the formulation of probability statements. We are concerned here with a probability statement which specifies the relative frequency with which a sample statistic of a given value or larger occurs in the sampling distribution. Let us suppose that we are given the value of a statistic computed from a random sample of measures from a universe normally distributed on some variable. Let us suppose, too, that the frequency function which describes the sampling distribution of the statistic is known and that the characteristics of the function have been determined. We can then ascertain the probability associated with the given value of the statistic. In other words, we can state the relative frequency with which statistics of equal or greater value than the one given are found in the sampling distribution.

Let us consider next the theoretical comparison of components of variability.

Imagine that two random samples are obtained from a universe and that the measures are arranged before us in two columns, each column corresponding to a sample. The total variability in these measures can be analyzed into two components, between-sample and within-sample. The between-sample sum of squares would be computed from the column or sample sums by means of formula (4.3). The within-sample sum of squares would be computed by combining the sum of squares for the first sample and the sum of squares for the second sample, after each had been computed by formula (4.1).

In the situation described above, differences between and differences within the samples would be the consequence of sampling, by random methods, from a varied population. Consequently, both components of variability can properly be described as components of sampling variability. Both components would reflect the variability or heterogeneity which is characteristic of the universe of measures. That is to say, the greater the variability of the universe, the greater each of these components will be, on the average, over all of the possible choices of pairs of samples.

The differences between samples can be compared to the differences within samples. The comparison is accomplished by computing a ratio, a statistic known as F. Let us defer for a moment the computational details. The important point about this ratio is not just that it compares these two components of variability but that all the possible chance outcomes of such comparisons can be determined. That is to say, the sampling distribution of F is known. The mathematical function which describes the sampling distribution of F is commonly referred to as the *F function*. Knowing the sampling distribution of the statistic F is equivalent to knowing all the possible comparison outcomes in the random selection of two samples and makes it possible to formulate a probability statement with respect to any one of those outcomes.

The student should recall that the logical evaluation discussed earlier required of the experimenter that he know all the possible chance outcomes of his experiment in order that he could specify the small proportion of chance outcomes he was willing to mistake for real ones. Information about the F function can be employed in formulating a probability statement, thereby making this specification possible. The necessary information has been tabulated and is widely available in tables such as those in the appendix. In the next chapter, the relevance of the F ratio to the evaluation of an experiment will be elaborated at some length. In addition, the formal, standard procedures for its use and interpretation will be described.

THE COMPARISON

The F ratio, the statistic used to compare components of random variation, does not compare sums of squares directly. Variances are first obtained from the sums of squares and then F is computed by taking the ratio of one variance to the other. The comparison of special interest to the experimenter involves the between-sample variance, computed from the between-sample sum of squares, and the within-sample variance, computed from the within-sample sum of squares.

Each of the variances employed in the F ratio is computed by dividing a sum of squares by a number of *degrees of freedom*. The between-sample variance is the between-sample sum of squares divided by $(c - 1)$ where c is the number of samples. The within-sample variance is the corresponding sum of squares divided by $(N - c)$, where N is the total number of observations and c is again the number of samples. F is the ratio of the between-sample variance to the within-sample variance. If we let V_b be the between-sample variance and V_w be the within-sample variance, then

$$F = \frac{V_b}{V_w}.$$

ESTIMATING ERROR

A comment on variances computed with degrees of freedom seems appropriate.

Means of random samples vary. We speak of this variation as *sampling error* and know that its magnitude depends on the population variance, σ^2, and the number of observations per sample, n. In fact, the variance of a sampling distribution of means is known to be σ^2/n.

When σ^2 is unknown, we may wish to estimate its value from a sample. That is, we might say we desire an *estimate of error*—an estimate of the magnitude of error variation that will affect our sampling.

Given a random sample of n observations, one could compute a variance, V, by the formula

$$V = \frac{\Sigma y^2}{n}.$$

Imagine now the sampling distribution of V. It would be a frequency distribution of values of V for all possible random samples of size n. Consider for a moment the average value of V, which we shall call $\bar{V}$, and the relation of this average to σ^2, the variance of the population from which the samples have been drawn. $\bar{V}$ would be smaller than σ^2 and V is said, therefore, to be an underestimate or a *biased* estimate of σ^2.

It is possible to correct the sample variance for this bias so that the average sample variance would be exactly equal to the population variance. The correction can be achieved by dividing the sum of squares by $(n - 1)$ instead of n. That is, an unbiased estimate, V_u, is given by the formula

$$V_u = \frac{\Sigma y^2}{(n - 1)}.$$

The sampling distribution of V_u has this characteristic:

$$\bar{V}_u = \sigma^2.$$

The proof that dividing by $(n - 1)$ yields an unbiased estimate will not be given here. The student may wish to consult a standard text in mathematical statistics for the demonstration.

Unbiased estimates can also be computed from two or more samples. One possibility is to combine the within-sample sums of squares and divide by $(N - c)$. This estimate is the denominator, V_w, in the F ratio of the preceding section. Another possibility is to divide the between-sample sum of squares by $(c - 1)$. This estimate is the numerator, V_b, in the F ratio of the preceding section.

PRACTICE

Let us turn from theory to practice. The point of major concern is the accuracy of the probability statement, which will depend on the degree of correspondence between theory and practice. The important question is: By what set of operations can an investigator hope to implement sampling theory sufficiently well to make reasonably accurate probability statements about his statistical comparisons? He cannot expect his practice to correspond exactly to the theory. He can, however, engage in certain procedures which have been found to be reasonable approximations to the requirements of the theory. When his procedures do approximate the requirements, the investigator is then in a position to compare components of variability in real data and to make satisfactorily accurate probability statements about the comparison.

The experimenter must choose his materials from some accessible supply. In psychological research, the supply will be an existent and available group or collection of human or animal subjects. The supply from which the experimenter actually obtains subjects corresponds to the theoretical universe or population.

A response variable is selected according to the interests and purposes of the investigator. Measures on the response variable for the supply of subjects, if these measures were obtained, should be normally distributed. That distributions encountered in actual practice often depart from normality is now widely recognized. For the moment, let us limit our discussion to those instances in which the departures from normality are not serious. A decision as to whether or not departures are serious should be made by the investigator. The decision should be based on consideration of the size of the samples, the number of score intervals in the distribution of responses, evidence as to the skewness and kurtosis of the supply, and the size of the supply in relation to the size of the samples. Any set of criterion values employed by the investigator in making this decision would be arbitrary and would have to be defended. Later on, we shall present some evidence as to the consequences of nonnormality, which information could be used in the choice and justification of such a set of criterion values.

The supply of subjects is enumerated; that is, subjects are numbered ordinally in any arbitrary order. The requirement that the units of the supply be numbered does not imply that the experimenter actually must gain access to and handle each unit during the enumeration. In psychological research, for example, ordinal numbers can often be applied to the names in a list of individuals in the supply.

A predetermined number of subjects is then selected for each sample. Subjects are selected by referring to the ordinal numbers of individuals in the supply. The selection is guided by the sequence of numbers in a table which has been subjected to certain tests of randomness. Since the sequence of these numbers is independent of the experimenter's personal judgment and the characteristics of his subjects, the numbers are an invaluable aid to research. Tables of random sampling numbers have been constructed and published by Fisher and Yates,[1] Kendall and Smith,[2] RAND Corporation,[4] and Tippett.[4]

THE UNIFORMITY TRIAL

Theoretical random sampling has its empirical counterpart in the uniformity trial. Suppose that two samples of subjects have been drawn from a supply by the method described above, in which a table of random numbers is employed. If we measure the subjects in the two samples under uniform conditions on a selected response variable, we complete what is known as a *uniformity trial*. It should be apparent that a uniformity trial differs from an actual experiment. In an experiment the samples would be measured under different conditions, not under uniform conditions. Our purpose in describing the uniformity trial is to give an account of the operations which are necessary for implementing sampling theory. The uniformity trial is sampling reality. The uniformity trial is sampling theory realized in practice.

A word of caution may be appropriate. We do not mean to imply that an experimenter must actually conduct a uniformity trial before he performs an experiment. What we do mean is that, for any given experiment, he should be able to describe a realistic uniformity trial whose operations will actually be incorporated in the experimental procedure and whose components of random sampling variability correspond to sources of variablity in the experiment. If he can describe and is prepared to conduct a uniformity trial appropriate to a given experiment, then his planning is such that the errors affecting the experiment will be random. In other words, components of variability in experimental data should in fact contain or be subject to the sampling error which can be demonstrated in a uniformity trial.

If the investigator does actually carry out the procedures of the uniformity trial, he will obtain two samples of observations possessing variability. The total variability of these measures of response can be analyzed into two components, the between-sample sum of squares and the combined within-sample sum of squares. The differences between and within samples are a direct consequence of the mechanical selection of subjects from a heterogeneous supply.

The comparison of components of variability is now possible. To make this comparison, the investigator computes an F ratio, the ratio of the between-sample variance to the combined within-sample variance.

A probability statement can now be made about the F ratio. The probability statement will indicate the relative frequency with which ratios of equal or greater magnitude occur in the sampling distribution or among all the possible comparison outcomes. The investigator refers to a table of F with the two sets of degrees of freedom used in computing the two variances in the ratio.* The information given in the table for the F function identified by that particular combination of degrees of freedom permits him to associate a probability with that ratio.

In statistical theory, the F function, the frequency function of the variance ratio, has been derived by mathematical methods. Its appropriateness can be demonstrated empirically as well. If the uniformity trials are continued until a very large number of variance ratios has been obtained, the frequency distribution of those ratios will roughly approximate a particular F function. Many empirical demonstrations of the appropriateness of the various frequency functions have been performed, thereby increasing our confidence in the use and application of sampling theory and sampling statistics in research.

---

* See Table A in the Appendix.

SUMMARY

Two basic propositions have now been elaborated. The first is that variability can be measured and analyzed. The second is that, in theory and in practice, components of variability can be compared and probability statements can be made about the comparisons.

REFERENCES

1. Fisher, R. A., and Yates F., *Statistical Tables for Biological, Agricultural and Medical Research.*   Edinburgh: Oliver & Boyd, Ltd., 1943.
2. Kendall, M. G., and Smith, B. B., *Tables of Random Sampling Numbers, No. 24.* London: Cambridge University Press, 1940.
3. RAND Corporation, *A Million Random Digits With 100,000 Normal Deviates.* Glencoe, Illinois: The Free Press, Publishers, 1955.
4. Tippett, L. H. C., *Tables of Random Sampling Numbers, Tracts for Computers, No. 15.*   London: Cambridge University Press, 1927.

THE FORMAL
EXPERIMENT

An experiment can be thought of as a combination of a uniformity trial and a treatment plan. The investigator carries out the operations of a uniformity trial, except that he imposes different treatments, according to a plan appropriate to his purposes. The operations of the uniformity trial insure a random or chance outcome for the experiment when the treatments have no differential effect. Incorporating the operations of the uniformity trial justifies his use of probability statements to characterize the result.

The possibility of comparing components or sources of variability, in theory and in practice, has been suggested. In the theoretical example of sampling, and in the uniformity trial, the magnitude of any difference is, by definition, the direct consequence of random sampling. In experimental data, another influence contributes to the variability. In an experiment, differences produced by varying treatments combine with sampling differences. Therein lies the problem of evaluation, for, wherever an observed difference is the result of both sampling and treatment, the part due to sampling and the part due to treatment cannot be separated.

If an experiment is to be evaluated, there must be, in the data, a component of variability which can be ascribed to sampling error alone. The magnitude of this component indicates the magnitude of the errors which affected the experiment in the selection of materials from a heterogeneous supply. The other necessary component of variability in the data—let us call it the *apparent* effect of the treatments—is attributable to the combined influence of sampling and treatment. The evaluation of the experiment involves the comparison of these two components.

48

Consider now, in broad outline, a conceptualization of the conduct of a simple experiment. The treatment plan for the single, independent variable consists of two conditions, *A* and *B*. The investigator obtains two random samples of subjects from a large supply, employing a table of random numbers to guide the selection. He has already chosen a dependent variable whose distribution, let us assume, is approximately normal. The investigator imposes condition *A* on one sample and condition *B* on the other sample, and measures the responses of subjects in both samples.

The arrangement of conditions and subjects and the recording of observations are represented schematically in Table 6.1. If there are differences

Table 6.1
THE ARRANGEMENT OF CONDITIONS AND SUBJECTS, AND THE RECORDING OF OBSERVATIONS FOR A SIMPLE SINGLE-VARIABLE EXPERIMENT

Conditions

A	B
Sample 1	Sample 2
Y_{11}	Y_{12}
Y_{21}	Y_{22}
$\vdots$	$\vdots$
Y_{i1}	Y_{i2}
$\vdots$	$\vdots$
Y_{n1}	Y_{n2}

among the subjects in the supply, these differences will be reflected in the measures, Y_{ik}, on the dependent variable. If conditions *A* and *B* have different effects on the responses, these effects will also be contained in the measures. The total variability in the observations obtained by the experimenter will contain both kinds of differences.

ADDITIVITY

Before going on to the analysis and evaluation of the experimental data, we should examine more closely the nature of treatment effects—the differences produced by the treatments. Treatment effects may be classified logically into two categories: those that are constant and additive and those that are not. Treatment effects are constant and additive when a given treatment produces the same increment (or decrement) of response for every subject in the sample receiving that treatment.

The effects of treatments A and B may be constant and additive, but different. When they differ, we say that the differential effects of A and B are constant and additive. For example, if A has the effect of increasing the magnitude of responses by two units and B has the effect of decreasing their magnitude by one unit, then the differential effect, a constant additive one, is three units.

Nonadditive effects cannot be described so simply, because of the variety of such effects that are possible. Treatment A may affect different subjects in different ways, and so may treatment B.

Consider first the case of constant and additive effects. Earlier, in the brief comment on estimates of error, the point was made that an unbiased estimate of the variance of the population could be computed from two random samples of observations by combining the within-sample sums of squares and dividing by the combined number of degrees of freedom. What happens to this unbiased estimate in an experiment involving two different treatments for the two samples? Nothing happens when the treatment effects are constant and additive. In this case, the estimate computed from the samples is not affected in any way and remains an unbiased estimate.

It is easy to verify the statement that the sample variances are unaffected by constant, additive treatment effects. Adding a constant value to each number in a set of numbers does not change the variability of the set. Consider the numbers

$$3, 4, 2, 1, 5.$$

Add two units to each one. The new set consists of the numbers

$$5, 6, 4, 3, 7.$$

Is the new set more or less varied? Neither. The variability is the same in both cases. That it is the same can be proved by computing the sum of squares for each set. In computing the sum of squares for the second set, it becomes apparent that, when a constant was added to each value, the same constant was added to the mean. In subtracting the new mean from each new value to obtain its deviation, the constants cancel and the deviation remains unchanged, thus leaving the sum of squares also unchanged. So it is that constant, additive treatment effects do not change the sample sums of squares and the combined within-sample variance. The variability within each sample is attributable to sampling and the magnitude of this variability provides a clue as to the magnitude of errors affecting the experiment.

Nonadditive treatment effects can change the variability within a sample and thereby pose a special problem in evaluation to be dealt with later. For the moment, let us assume that the effects of treatments A and B in the simple experiment under consideration are approximately constant and additive.

It was also stated in the comments on estimates of error that an unbiased estimate of the population variance could be computed from the between-sample sum of squares. What effect will the constant additive effects of treatments A and B have on this estimate? If the effect of A is different from that of B, the estimate will be biased. This is simply to say that the between-sample sum of squares will be larger, on the average, than it would be if there were no difference between the effect of A and that of B.

Since differential effects of the treatments combine with sampling error, the final observed difference between the samples will contain both sampling error and treatment effects. What part of the variability is due to sampling and what part is due to treatment will not be known to the experimenter. Neither the relative magnitudes nor the directions of the two influences can be distinguished.

The simple experiment described above in general terms involved two samples of subjects, a response variable having an approximately normal distribution, and two treatments, the effects of which are approximately constant and additive on all respondents. In the data from the experiment, two sources of variability can be identified. One source contains only sampling variability and provides the basis for an unbiased estimate of the heterogeneity of the supply of subjects. The other source, which is to be evaluated, contains both sampling and treatment variability in unknown amounts.

THE EVALUATION

The differences between the two treatments, A and B, as they appear in the observations obtained from the two samples, are suspect. That is, there is considerable doubt as to whether the treatments produced the differences or any part of them. The apparent differences between A and B could be due entirely to sampling error.

It is a fundamental principle in evaluation that the greater the differences among individuals in the supply, the larger will be the errors to which the experimental comparison is liable and the more suspect will be the observed differences between the samples. Let us examine this principle more closely. Suppose we have before us an observed difference between the means of conditions *A* and *B*. When subjects are relatively heterogeneous, random selection will often produce a difference as large as, or larger than, the one observed. On the other hand, when subjects are relatively homogeneous, selection will seldom produce such a difference or a larger one, and it is more likely to be due to the differential effects of *A* and *B*.

It follows that the investigator, in evaluating his experiment, should compare the between-sample variance with the within-sample variance. It is logical to do so because the between-sample variance is a measure of the treatment effect contaminated by error and the within-sample variance is a measure or estimate of the error which is responsible for the contamination. The within-sample variance tells the investigator the size of the errors which, in being randomly distributed over the two samples, may actually have produced the between-sample variance. Comparison of the two variances tells him how likely it is that this is so. If the experimenter learns that the apparent treatment differences are small compared to the errors which could have produced them, he will not decide that treatments *A* and *B* have different effects. On the other hand, if he learns that the apparent treatment differences are large compared to the errors, he can decide with some confidence that treatments *A* and *B* do have different effects.

According to the argument of the preceding paragraph, the experimenter's decision that treatments *A* and *B* do have different effects is based on the occurrence of what might be called *favorable* results. The difficulty, of course, is that favorable results can occur by chance, and those due to chance alone are not distinguishable from those due to real effects. Recognizing this fact, the investigator can only limit the size of the class of chance effects about which he is willing to be mistaken. The standard procedure for making the comparison of treatment and error and, at the same time, allowing for the occurrence of favorable results by chance is a statistical test of significance.

THE TEST OF SIGNIFICANCE

As a first step in applying a test of significance to experimental data, the investigator adopts the viewpoint that the observed differences between the conditions are due only to sampling errors. The viewpoint is not unrealistic since, if the treatments have not produced differences, random selection will have determined the outcome. The viewpoint is given formal expression in a statement of the *null hypothesis*, a hypothesis that there are no treatment differences. The investigator then decides on the size of the class of most favorable chance outcomes that he is willing to mistake for real effects.

The size of the class is expressed as a proportion and is called the *level of significance*. A proportion of 1 in 20 or 0.05 is widely employed in this connection. The proportion 0.01 is also frequently used. The choice of a level of significance determines a criterion value of F, which can be obtained from a table of the F function.* The criterion value is one that is equaled or exceeded in the sampling distribution by the proportion specified as the level of significance.

The experimenter computes an F ratio from his data and compares it with the criterion value. If the obtained value equals or exceeds the criterion, it falls in the class of chance outcomes he is willing to regard as real, and he abandons the viewpoint he adopted; that is, he rejects the null hypothesis. If the obtained value of F is smaller than the criterion, it falls in the class of chance outcomes to be treated as such, and he retains the viewpoint; that is, he accepts the null hypothesis. The decision in either case may be an erroneous one. He may reject the null hypothesis when there is no treatment difference; he may accept the null hypothesis when there actually is a treatment difference.

The choice of a level of significance is arbitrary; there is no absolute criterion. The arbitrary nature of the choice actually makes it possible for an experimenter, if he so chooses, to adjust his level of significance from one occasion to another and thus favor the announcement of a preponderance of significant results. Such practices have been widely criticized, and there is common acceptance of the principle that a level of significance should be chosen before the data have been examined by the investigator. When the level of significance is fixed in advance of an experiment and kept constant throughout repetitions of it, incorrect decisions to reject the null hypothesis will occur with the relative frequency indicated by the level of significance. When the level of significance is shifted, on the basis of the results and the inclinations of the investigator, the probability of an incorrect rejection is indeterminate.

Saying that the level of significance should be kept constant throughout repetitions of an experiment does not mean that it should be the same in all research. Practical considerations with respect to the risk involved in making an erroneous decision will often influence the choice of a level of significance. For example, if an administrative decision involving the expenditure of a large sum of money depends on the decision to accept or reject the null hypothesis, the experimenter will likely choose a satisfactorily small probability value as the level of significance so that erroneous decisions are not as likely to occur. Even though the same level of significance may

* See Table A in the Appendix.

not be appropriate for all experimentation, the choice can still be made in advance and maintained throughout the course of experimentation on a given problem.

A TEST OF ADDITIVITY

In the evaluation just discussed, an assumption was made that the effect of each treatment was constant and additive on the responses of the subjects in the sample on which the treatment was imposed.   There is a test of significance for making a decision as to whether or not the assumption is justified. The test employs a variance ratio.   We have said that a nonadditive treatment effect can change the variability within a sample and that differential nonadditive treatment effects can produce heterogeneous sample variances. That is, if treatment *A* has a nonadditive effect and treatment *B* has a different nonadditive effect, their respective sample variances may differ, on the average, and cannot be taken as unbiased estimates of the same population variance.

Many kinds of nonadditive treatment effects may be detected by comparing one sample variance with another, that is, by testing the homogeneity of the two variances.   The test of significance involves an *F* ratio, the ratio of the variance of one sample to the variance of the other.   A sample variance is computed by dividing the sample sum of squares by $(n - 1)$.

The null hypothesis is that any observed difference between the two sample variances is due to sampling error.   After the level of significance is chosen, the ratio of the two sample variances is computed.   Reference is then made to a table of *F* for the criterion value of the ratio for the two numbers of degrees of freedom in the two samples.   If the obtained *F* is larger than the criterion value, the null hypothesis is rejected and a conclusion is reached that the variances are heterogeneous and that the effects of the treatments are nonadditive.   If the obtained *F* is smaller than the criterion, then the null hypothesis is accepted and the conclusion reached that the variances are homogeneous and that the assumption of additive treatment effects is justified.

When it appears that the treatment effects are not constant and additive, then the interpretation of results from the main evaluation of the experiment should be appropriately qualified.   The nature of the qualification will be considered when the consequences of nonadditivity are presented.

EVALUATION OF THE CHEATING EXPERIMENT

The data from the experiment concerned with the effect of instructions on cheating, which were presented in Table 2.1, will be analyzed below.   We shall choose a probability value of 0.05 as the level of significance.

The total variability in the 37 observations can be analyzed into two components, between- and within-samples. The between-sample sum of squares represents the apparent, differential effects of the two sets of instructions. The within-sample sum of squares is a measure of error. The total sum of squares and its two components are computed below. The formulas for the three components are given along with the summary values to be substituted in the formulas.

The formula for the total sum of squares, (4.2), is

$$\Sigma Y^2 - C'.$$

The summary data required are:

$$\Sigma Y = 116,$$
$$(\Sigma Y)^2 = 13{,}456,$$
$$N = 37,$$
$$C' = (\Sigma Y)^2 / N = 13{,}456/37 = 363.68,$$
$$\Sigma Y^2 = 1030.$$

Computation of the total sum of squares:

$$1030 - 363.68 = 666.32.$$

The formula for the within-sample sum of squares for any sample, (4.1), is

$$\Sigma Y^2 - \frac{(\Sigma Y)^2}{n}.$$

The summary data required for the control group are:

$$\Sigma Y = 79,$$
$$(\Sigma Y)^2 = 6241,$$
$$n = 19,$$
$$\Sigma Y^2 = 683.$$

Computation of the sum of squares for the control group:

$$683 - 6241/19 = 683 - 328.47 = 354.53.$$

The summary data required for the reward group are:

$$\Sigma Y = 37,$$
$$(\Sigma Y)^2 = 1369,$$
$$n = 18,$$
$$\Sigma Y^2 = 347.$$

Computation of the sum of squares for the reward group:

$$347 - 1369/18 = 347 - 76.06 = 270.94.$$

Combining the sums of squares for the two groups:

$$354.53 + 270.94 = 625.47.$$

The formula for the between-sample sum of squares, (4.3), adapted for a varying n as described on page 00 is:

$$\frac{\left(\sum_i Y_{i1}\right)^2}{n_1} + \frac{\left(\sum_i Y_{i2}\right)^2}{n_2} - C'.$$

The summary data required are:

$$\sum_i Y_{i1} = \text{the sum for the control group} = 79,$$
$$\sum_i Y_{i2} = \text{the sum for the reward group} = 37,$$
$$n_1 = 19,$$
$$n_2 = 18,$$
$$C' = 363.68$$

Computation of the between-sample sum of squares:

$$79^2/19 + 37^2/18 - 363.68 = 40.85.$$

Before proceeding to the main evaluation, we can check our computation by summing the two components and comparing the sum with the total sum of squares. We find that

$$666.32 = 40.85 + 625.47.$$

The main evaluation of the experiment can now be undertaken by computing the between-sample variance, the combined within-sample variance, and the ratio of the former to the latter. The between-sample sum of squares is 40.85, and the between-sample variance, V_b, computed with $(c - 1) = 1$ degree of freedom, is

$$V_b = \frac{40.85}{1} = 40.85.$$

The combined within-sample sum of squares is 625.47 and the corresponding variance, V_w, computed with $(N - c) = 35$ degrees of freedom, is

$$V_w = \frac{625.47}{35} = 17.87.$$

F, the ratio of the between-sample variance to the within-sample variance, is

$$F = \frac{V_b}{V_w} = \frac{40.85}{17.87} = 2.28.$$

The criterion value of F associated with the 0.05 level of significance for 1 and 35 degrees of freedom is 4.12.* The obtained value of 2.28 is less than 4.12. We accept the null hypothesis and conclude that the difference between the two samples, as reflected by the means, is due to sampling error.

The conventional presentation of these various quantities is shown in Table 6.2. The tabular presentation permits the reader of a research report to examine the results quickly and efficiently.

Table 6.2
ANALYSIS OF VARIANCE FOR THE EXPERIMENT ON CHEATING

Component of variability	SS	df	V	F	F_c
Between control and reward conditions	40.85	1	40.85	2.28	4.12
Combined within-sample or error	625.47	35	17.87	—	—
Total	666.32	36	—	—	—

SS = sum of squares
df = degrees of freedom
F_c = criterion value of F for 0.05 level of significance

We should next test the homogeneity of the two sample variances for evidence of nonadditivity of the effects of the instructions. For the control group, the sum of squares is 354.53 and the variance, computed with $(n_1 - 1)$ = 18 degrees of freedom is

$$\frac{354.53}{18} = 19.70.$$

For the reward group, the sum of squares is 270.94 and the variance, computed with $(n_2 - 1) = 17$ degrees of freedom is

$$\frac{270.94}{17} = 15.94.$$

Since the table of F usually gives only values of the ratio equal to or greater than one, in other words, one tail of the distribution of F, we compute the ratio of the larger to the smaller as

$$F = \frac{19.70}{15.94} = 1.24.$$

* The value was obtained by interpolation from Table A in the Appendix.

Placing the larger variance over the smaller, in the long run, doubles the expected number of ratios greater than one. To compensate, we halve the probability value, making it 0.025, in order to operate at the 0.05 level of significance. The criterion value of F, associated with the probability 0.025, for the two numbers of degrees of freedom, 18 and 17, is 2.65.* The obtained value is less than the criterion and we again accept the null hypothesis. There is no evidence of nonadditive treatment effects.

The simplest form of the single variable experiment, the form described above, involves two conditions or treatments and two samples of subjects. The design can be enlarged, however, to include any number of conditions for the single independent variable. The several conditions may differ among themselves qualitatively or quantitatively. An example of an independent variable involving qualitative differences would be a set of four different methods of instruction applied to four samples of human subjects. Examples of quantitative conditions would be four levels of food deprivation, periods of 0, 8, 16, and 24 hours duration, conditions which might be imposed on four samples of animals in a psychological experiment. The general form of the analysis of variance for c conditions is given in Table 6.3.

Table 6.3
GENERAL FORM OF THE ANALYSIS OF VARIANCE FOR A SINGLE-VARIABLE DESIGN

Component	df	V	F
Between samples or treatments	$c - 1$	V_b	V_b/V_w
Within samples or error	$N - c$	V_w	
Total	$N - 1$		

c = number of conditions = number of samples
N = total number of subjects

Computation for the main evaluation of an experiment having more than two conditions and samples can be accomplished by means of formulas (4.1), (4.2), and (4.3). The test for homogeneity of sample variances can also be extended to any number of samples. Although other tests are available, a test devised by Bartlett[1] is widely used and is described in the next section.

* The value was obtained by interpolation from Table B in the Appendix.

BARTLETT'S TEST OF HOMOGENEITY

Let c = the number of samples,

n_k = the number of observations in the kth sample,

N = the total number of observations.

Bartlett's test involves computation of a quantity whose sampling distribution is given by a chi square function. Steps in the computation are given below.

1. Compute the combined within-sample variance, V_w, by dividing the combined within-sample sum of squares by $(N - c)$ degrees of freedom:

$$V_w = \frac{\Sigma \Sigma y^2}{(N - c)}.$$

2. Find the common logarithm of V_w and multiply it by $(N - c)$:

$$(N - c) \log V_w.$$

3. Compute the variance of each sample, V_k, with $(n_k - 1)$ degrees of freedom:

$$V_k = \frac{\Sigma y^2}{(n_k - 1)}.$$

4. Find the common logarithm of each V_k, multiply each logarithm by $(n_k - 1)$, and sum these c products:

$$\Sigma(n_k - 1) \log V_k.$$

Note: When $(n_k - 1)$ is a constant, it can be written before the summation sign.

5. Compute the difference, D, as follows:

$$D = (N - c)\log V_w - \Sigma(n_k - 1)\log V_k.$$

6. Compute a factor, f, as follows:

$$f = \frac{2.3026}{E},$$

where 2.3026 is a constant and

$$E = 1 + \frac{1}{3(c - 1)}\left[\Sigma \frac{1}{(n_k - 1)} - \frac{1}{(N - c)}\right].$$

Note: When $(n_k - 1)$ is a constant, the summation in the computation of E can be simplified.

7. Compute the statistic chi square, χ^2, for $(c - 1)$ degrees of freedom:

$$\chi^2 = fD.$$

8. Consult a table of chi square to determine the probability associated with the obtained value (see Table C in the Appendix). Accept or reject the null hypothesis. Accepting the null hypothesis is taken as justifying the assumption that sample variances are homogeneous and treatment effects are constant and additive.

An example of Bartlett's test has been worked out and displayed on page 157.

THE COMPLETE ACT OF RANDOMIZATION

Our discussion of the errors to which experiments are liable has been deliberately oversimplified. The only errors which have been considered are those attributable to the random sampling of subjects from a heterogeneous supply. Heterogeneity in the supply is one important source of errors, but there is another. This second source of error includes an unspecifiable number of uncontrolled influences associated with the measuring instrument, the act of making an observation, and the time and place of measurement. In general, when we speak of sampling variability or sampling error in an experiment, we have in mind the combined effect of both sources of error, the subject and the occasion of measurement.

Each observation in the experimental data depends on the characteristics of a subject who differs from other subjects and on an unknown number of uncontrolled influences that jointly produce at the moment of measurement a certain bias in the observation. The combination of errors from these two sources results in an observation subject to an error of unknown magnitude and direction. If, in addition to the random selection of subjects, the experimenter arranges for the random conjunction of a given treatment, a subject, and an occasion of measurement, a random distribution of error will be produced over all of his observations. This complete act of randomization renders the bias from the combination of errors predictable on the basis of sampling theory.

Let us take another view of this important issue. Suppose, for example, that 20 observations are to be made in a simple experiment involving two conditions and two random samples. Ten of these observations will be made under one condition and ten under the other. Disregarding for the moment the two treatments, we must acknowledge that the 20 observations will necessarily be made in as many different settings. No effort on the part of the experimenter will guarantee identical contexts for these observations. The information upon which an evaluation of the experiment will depend will be contained in and limited to the 20 observations.

Any like influences on all of the measurements will not bias the comparison and can therefore be ignored. Only the unintended differences among the measures constitute a bias. The occurrence of differences arising from the different treatments, since they are intended and are the object of investigation, do not trouble us. Random distribution of the unintended influences and their differences over the 20 observations is part of the random distribution of errors to which the experiment should be liable. Combined with random sampling, the act of randomization thus guarantees that the laws of chance will govern the bias of the experiment, a bias which our method of evaluation takes account of. Random selection of subjects and random assignment of subjects to treatments and to occasions of measurement are operations which can actually be carried out by the experimenter to insure a random outcome when there is, in fact, no treatment effect.

Stating that the experimenter should randomly assign subjects to treatments and to occasions of measurement is a very general way of describing randomization as it should apply to any experiment. It is not practical or even possible to specify in exact detail here the randomization procedures appropriate to every kind of experiment. The requirements will vary from one problem to another and from one area of investigation to another. Only the expert in a given content area will know enough about that area to plan effective randomization procedures and to implement the general principle of assigning subjects randomly to treatments and to occasions of measurement.

SUMMARY

The selection and assigning of subjects to experimental conditions is a critical operation in the conduct of a psychological experiment. Pre-experimental differences among subjects constitute large potential errors that can seriously bias the comparison. Using a separate group of subjects for each treatment has the advantage of eliminating bias arising from repeated treatment and measurement. Replication is necessary if the experimenter is to obtain information as to the magnitude of the errors to which his experiment is liable. Random selection and assignment of subjects to treatments eliminates the experimenter's personal bias as an issue and renders the bias predictable on the basis of probability theory. The complete procedure of randomization includes, in addition to random selection and assignment to conditions, the random assignment to occasions of measurement. Formal evaluation involves the use of a test of significance in which components of variability are compared and a decision is made as to the outcome of the experiment.

AN ALTERNATIVE METHOD OF EVALUATION

The test of significance involving the F ratio is not the only formal method of evaluating the results of the single-variable experiment employing random samples.   There are other methods which are sometimes used to advantage. All of these methods have had their development within the context of statistical inference and sampling theory and are, essentially, statistical methods of making the comparison called for by the experiment and a decision as to the outcome.   All of these methods, including the so-called non-parametric or distribution-free techniques, require the randomization of errors.

Chief among the alternative methods is the test of significance based on the statistic, t, and its sampling distribution, the t function.   The ratio of the difference between sample means to the standard error of the difference is a statistic distributed as the t function.   The difference between means is the quantity to be evaluated.   It is compared with the standard error, which is a function of the variability within the samples.   The t ratio thus makes the same comparison of apparent treatment differences and error as does the F ratio.   The formula for the t ratio is

$$t = \frac{\bar{Y}_{.1} - \bar{Y}_{.2}}{S\sqrt{(1/n_1 + 1/n_2)}},$$

where $S = \sqrt{V_w}$. (For computation of V_w, see page 43.) Also $n_1 =$ number of subjects in the first sample; $n_2 =$ number of subjects in the second sample.

In a single-variable experiment with two samples, the use of t when the expected direction of the difference between means is unspecified, a so-called *two-tailed test*, will lead to exactly the same decision as the F test.   As a matter of fact, $t^2 = F$, in the case of two samples, when one degree of freedom is associated with the treatment effect.   When the direction of the difference between means has been specified, in what is called a *one-tailed test*, the experimenter has, in effect, chosen to disregard differences in the other direction regardless of their magnitude.   A smaller difference in the specified direction will then be required to meet or exceed the criterion value, thus insuring that the one-tailed test will more often detect a treatment effect of a given magnitude than will the two-tailed test.   The F ratio can also be used in a one-tailed test if one disregards differences in the one direction and doubles the level of significance to compensate for the outcomes that are to be disregarded.

An error is often made by the beginning student in using t when c, the number of conditions, is greater than two.   He may compare each condition with every other one, determining the probability in each case as he would when $c = 2$, and thereby identify what appear to be one or more significant differences. The fallacy in such a procedure is that his level of significance is not actually what he chose. As $c(c - 1)/2$, the number of possible comparisons, increases so does the probability of obtaining any given number of significant t's. For instance, when $c > 2$, the probability of obtaining at least one significant t is greater than the chosen level of significance. The F test of the differences between c means is, of course, appropriate in evaluating the entire set of differences. The problem of testing particular comparisons is a thorny one, whether all possibilities are tried or only certain ones, and whether those that are tried are specified in advance of the experiment or after the data have been examined. The issues which surround this problem may be too difficult for the beginning student. Examination of a discussion by Ryan[2] is convincing proof of the complexity of the problem.

REFERENCES

1. Bartlett, M. S., "Properties of Sufficiency and Statistical Tests," *Proceedings of the Royal Society* (London). Series A, 160, 1937, 1-273.
2. Ryan, T. A., "Multiple Comparisons in Psychological Research," *Psychological Bulletin*, 56, 1959, 26-47.

INCORRECT DECISIONS

7

The formal evaluation of an experiment by means of a test of significance culminates in a decision on the part of the investigator to accept or reject the null hypothesis. In rejecting the null hypothesis, he may, of course, be making an incorrect decision. Even though a very large difference between conditions has been observed, that difference may be nothing more than an accumulation of random errors. On the other hand, accepting the null hypothesis can, on occasion, be an incorrect decision. When the real treatment effect is small and random errors are large, an accumulation of errors may cancel and obscure the treatment effect. The observed difference will not meet the criterion for significance and the null hypothesis will be accepted erroneously.

ERRORS OF THE FIRST KIND

If we reject the null hypothesis when we should accept it, we commit what is called an *error of the first kind*. The random outcomes of an experiment, including those outcomes which prompt errors of the first kind in our decisions, can be represented in a frequency distribution. For this purpose we shall refer again to the simple experiment involving two conditions and two samples of subjects.

Let us imagine that the two conditions are not different in their effects, that there really is no variation due to treatments. In the totality of outcomes which can be deduced for the experiment as consequences of sampling error, F, the ratio of the between-sample variance to the within-sample variance, will vary. The sampling distribution for F computed from

64

two large samples is shown in Fig. 7.1. Since we are considering a situation in which the null hypothesis is true and should be accepted, any rejections will be errors. If we choose a level of significance, thereby fixing the size of the class of chance outcomes we are willing to mistake for real ones, we can locate a point on the abscissa establishing a *region of rejection* in the right tail of the distribution. The region of rejection, usually designated by α, the Greek letter *alpha*, identifies the variance ratios whose occurrence will be the occasion for erroneous rejection of the null hypothesis. The region of rejection for the 0.05 level of significance is the shaded area in the right tail of the curve. The area is 0.05 of the total area under the curve in Fig. 7.1.

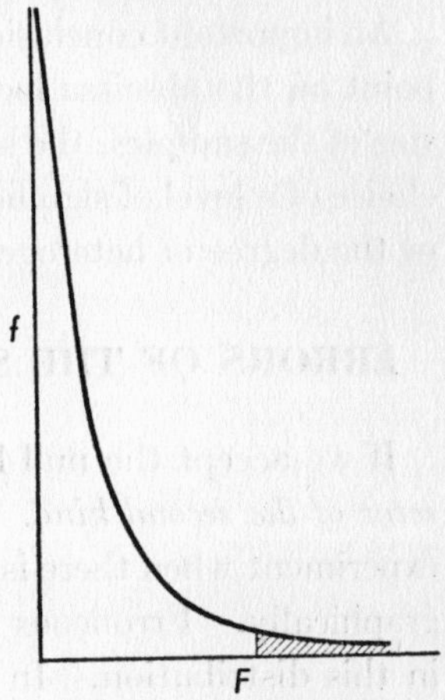

Let us examine the sampling distribution of F ratios more closely. The dispersion of the sampling distribution depends on the size of the samples. As the size of samples increases, the dispersion is reduced. Consider the numerator and the denominator in the F ratio. The between-sample variance has a sampling distribution which is described by a chi-square function for $(c - 1)$ degrees of freedom. The mean of the sampling distribution is σ^2, the population variance. Increases in sample size do not affect this distribution. The within-sample variance has a sampling distribu-

Fig. 7.1 The sampling distribution of F, the ratio of the between-sample variance to the within-sample variance, under the null hypothesis, for two very large samples. Shaded area is the region of rejection.

tion given by a chi-square function for $(N - c)$ degrees of freedom. Its mean is also σ^2. For very small samples, the distribution of the within-sample variance is highly skewed in the positive direction, implying that the mode is below the mean and that there is a preponderance of small values of the within-sample variance. F ratios greater than some given value tend to arise from combinations involving small within-sample variances. As the size of samples increases, the distribution of the within-sample variance becomes more nearly symmetrical about σ^2 with a smaller dispersion, and the distribution approaches normality. The consequence is a reduction in the number of small values of the within-sample variance and large F ratios. Thus, to maintain any fixed proportion of values of F greater than some criterion value, the criterion value becomes smaller as the size of samples increases.

We should also note that the distribution of F, under the null hypothesis, does not depend on the magnitude of the population variance. Differences between means vary more when the population variance is larger, but so do sample variances. Differences between means vary less when the population variance is smaller but so do sample variances.

An important conclusion to be drawn from this discussion is that, while the point on the abscissa locating the region of rejection shifts according to the size of the samples, the size of the region of rejection depends directly on the choice of a level of significance and is not affected by either the size of samples or the degree of heterogeneity in the population.

ERRORS OF THE SECOND KIND

If we accept the null hypothesis when we should reject it, we commit an *error of the second kind.* The distribution of the totality of outcomes of an experiment when there is a given treatment difference can also be represented graphically. Erroneous acceptances of the null hypothesis can be identified in this distribution. In applying a test of significance, we always test the null hypothesis, but in speaking of an error of the second kind, we imply that an alternative hypothesis is, in fact, true. A representation of erroneous acceptances must, therefore, incorporate both notions, the null hypothesis and an alternative.

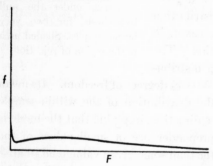

Fig. 7.2 The sampling distribution of F, the ratio of the between-sample variance to the within-sample variance, under an alternative hypothesis, for two very large samples.

The outcomes of an experiment under the null hypothesis have already been portrayed as the sampling distribution of F in Fig. 7.1. The outcomes, under an alternative hypothesis, will vary as a consequence of sampling error and can be displayed in another sampling distribution. The sampling distribution under an alternative hypothesis appears in Fig. 7.2.

Placing the two curves at appropriate positions on the same abscissa makes possible an interesting analysis of errors of the second kind in relation to (a) the level of significance, (b) the size of the samples, (c) the size of the real effect of the treatments, and (d) the heterogeneity of the population.

In Fig. 7.3, the sampling distribution of *F* under a given alternative hypothesis is drawn to the right of the curve for the null hypothesis. A point on the abscissa locating the region of rejection in the curve on the left has been chosen and the region of rejection, which has been shaded, is located in the right tail of the left distribution. When the alternative hypothesis is true, this same point on the abscissa distinguishes occasions for acceptance from occasions for rejection, but acceptances must now be considered errors and rejections must be considered correct decisions. The shaded area in the left tail of the curve at the right represents the region of erroneous acceptances or the probability of errors of the second kind, usually designated β (the Greek letter *beta*). The probability of a correct rejection is, of course, $(1 - \beta)$,

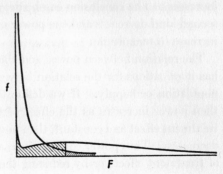

Fig. 7.3 The sampling distributions of *F*, the ratio of the between-sample variance to the within-sample variance, under the null hypothesis and a given alternative hypothesis, for two very large samples. Shaded area on the right is the region of erroneous rejections; shaded area on the left is the region of erroneous acceptances.

which quantity is termed the *power* of the test of significance.

We have said that the probability of errors of the second kind is a function of the level of significance. Consider what would happen to β in Fig. 7.3, if the region of rejection, α, were to be made smaller. Moving the point locating the boundary of the area to the right would enlarge β. That is, reducing the level of significance or the probability of errors of the first kind increases the probability of errors of the second kind and reduces the power of the test. On the other hand, increasing α would reduce β and increase $(1 - \beta)$.

Earlier, we stated that the scatter of the sampling distribution of *F* depended on the size of samples. With larger samples the spread is reduced. With smaller samples it is increased. With smaller samples, the overlap of the two distributions in Fig. 7.3 will be greater; the boundary of the region of rejection will be further to the right; β will be larger and $(1 - \beta)$ will be smaller. When larger samples are employed, the two curves will be more narrow, overlap will be less, the boundary will be further to the left, β will be smaller and $(1 - \beta)$ will be larger.

The presence of treatment differences has the effect of producing larger *F* ratios and thereby displacing the sampling distribution of *F* to the right as shown in Fig. 7.3. The larger the effects, the greater the displacement. It is apparent that the overlap of the two curves is reduced as this displacement increases. The conclusion can be drawn that the probability of errors of the second kind decreases and the power of the test increases as treatment effects increase in magnitude.

The relation between power and the effects of treatment, as stated above, has implications for the relation between power and the heterogeneity of the population or supply. If we define the population variance as a constant, then power increases as the effect of treatment increases. If we define the treatment effect as a constant, then power increases as the population variance decreases. Thus power could be increased either by increasing the magnitude of treatment effects or by reducing the magnitude of errors.

SUMMARY

The level of significance or the probability of errors of the first kind is directly the consequence of the experimenter's choice. The level of significance, being a matter of choice, is not influenced by the size of samples or the heterogeneity of the population.

The power of a test of significance is defined as the probability of a correct rejection of the null hypothesis or as one minus the probability of an error of the second kind. Increasing the level of significance increases power; reducing the level reduces power. Power is greater for larger samples than for smaller ones. Power is greater in the case of larger treatment effects than it is in the case of smaller ones. It is less for heterogeneous populations than for homogeneous ones.

ASSUMPTIONS

8

The importance of sampling theory and its assumptions in the evaluation of an experiment cannot be emphasized too much. A test of significance is based on a mathematical model. To the extent that the various properties of the model correspond to reality in the experimental situation, to that extent will use of the model produce knowledge. If there is no correspondence between the model and reality, then use of the model—perhaps it is better called *misuse*—does not and cannot contribute to knowledge.

It is an oversimplification of the problem, however, to speak of correspondence and noncorrespondence between the model and the experiment as if correspondence is a unidimensional and dichotomous characteristic. The model possesses a number of features. There may be correspondence between the model and the experimental situation with respect to some of these features and not others. Furthermore, the degree of correspondence with respect to any particular feature is an important consideration in reaching a conclusion as to the appropriateness of using the model in a given situation.

As a matter of fact, the experimenter, if he is to continue to do research, must reconcile himself to approximations in the relations between a model and the phenomenon he is investigating. Probably no model ever fit a behavioral situation exactly and, even if, in a rare instance, it did, the experimenter would not have evidence to that effect. Recognizing that one is, of necessity, limited to working with approximate rather than exact methods should not be distracting and discouraging for the student, although it sometimes appears to be so. Advances in knowledge are possible, although they are certainly difficult to achieve, in the world in which we live and with the methods at our disposal.

The sensible use of sampling theory in evaluating the results of research requires that the experimenter know the sampling model, its important features, and the respects in which correspondence is implied between features of the model and features of his experiment. Making these points of desired correspondence explicit is often referred to as *stating the assumptions* underlying a statistic. Fulfilling these assumptions is a primary concern of the experimenter. Fulfilling an assumption, however, does not mean that one simply assumes a certain proposition to be true when no pertinent evidence is available or when the evidence shows that the proposition is false. The student of statistics would do well to look upon assumptions as requirements and to understand that failure to meet these requirements may have serious consequences for his work.

The experimenter should also know the best methods of implementing the theoretical model. He must consider what steps he should take in the actual conduct of the experiment to guarantee, as much as possible, a sound evaluation. When one first approaches the problem, it is not immediately obvious what procedure is implied by the theoretical model. The mathematician states the requirements of the model in general and abstract terms, not specific and concrete ones. The elements of an experimental situation vary greatly from one field of investigation to another and from one problem to another within a given field. In the final analysis, a judgment on the part of the investigator is necessary in the choice of particular and concrete experimental operations. In the absence of a universal, absolute standard, the judgment is often a difficult one to make. Such judgments should be tested against the consensus of experienced colleagues.

Finally, the experimenter should be aware of the consequences of disparities between the model and the experimental situation. A disparity in one respect may be of no great consequence; in another, it may cast serious doubts on the value of the results of the entire experiment. Since disparities are the rule rather than the exception, he must be prepared to interpret his results with due consideration for the inadequacies of the experiment. He must qualify his interpretive statements accordingly and must, if possible, indicate the nature of the increase in error introduced in the experiment as a consequence of the failure to meet the requirements of the model.

VALIDITY

If all the requirements for the test of significance have been met perfectly, the probability of an error of the first kind is fixed by the experimenter's choice of a level of significance and is exactly equal to that criterion probability value. When any of the assumptions underlying the test have not been met, the actual probability of an error of the first kind may differ from the chosen level of significance. The magnitude of the difference depends on the assumption in question and on the extent to which it has not been fulfilled.

The fact that the probability of an erroneous rejection may differ from the level of significance suggests an important distinction between the *true* probability and the *nominal* probability of errors of the first kind. The *true* probability is the relative frequency with which erroneous rejections will actually occur under the circumstances obtaining in the experiment. The *nominal* probability is the level of significance chosen by the experimenter as indicating the proportion of chance results he is willing to mistake for real treatment effects. When the true and nominal probability values are equal and the proportion of erroneous rejections is then what the experimenter intended, we say the experiment is *valid*. The validity of an experiment can thus be expressed in terms of the discrepancy between the true probability and the nominal probability of errors of the first kind.

The validity of a test of significance in the analysis of variance depends on the fulfillment of requirements having to do with the population distribution, the method of selection, and the nature of the treatment effects. The population is assumed to be normally distributed. The method of selection is assumed to be random sampling. Treatment effects are assumed to be constant and additive.

CONSEQUENCES OF NONNORMALITY

A normal curve is a continuous function possessing a characteristic form or shape. The function is symmetrical around the mean of the distribution and mesokurtic, that is, neither flat nor peaked. It has a single mode and branches that approach but never reach the abscissa. A normal curve was shown in Fig. 5.1.

Departures from normality are commonly described in terms of discontinuity, asymmetry, and flatness or peakedness. Discontinuity can be characterized in terms of the number of class or score intervals in the population distribution. Asymmetry or skewness is usually measured by the third moment of the standardized measures. The formula for S, the measure of skewness, is

$$S = \frac{\Sigma z^3}{N},$$

where the z's are standard scores and N is the number of cases in the population. For a normal curve, $S = 0$. Kurtosis, the peakedness or flatness of such a curve, is measured by the fourth moment.   The formula for K, the measure of kurtosis, is

$$K = \frac{\Sigma z^4}{N}.$$

For a normal curve, $K = 3$, and the curve is said to be mesokurtic.

Although discontinuity, skewness, and kurtosis—and their effects—are interrelated in a complex fashion, it is worthwhile to discuss them separately.

A continuous population variable is one whose frequency distribution has an indefinitely large number of intervals.   In reality, all response variables, as measured, are discontinuous.   The degree of discontinuity varies, of course, from one kind of measurement to another.   In the measurement of physical attributes of response, such as time, distance, and force, the potential number of intervals may be very large.   In the measurement of physical dimensions of stimuli, as in psychophysics, again the degree of discontinuity may be slight.   A psychological test, scale, or inventory, however, even when it is administered to a very large number of individuals, seldom yields more than 100 score intervals and often yields as few as 20.   At the extreme of discontinuity are the dichotomous variables one occasionally encounters.

In trying to evaluate the effects of discontinuity, one must take account of the size of the samples as well as the number of intervals in the population distribution.   The effects of discontinuity are less serious for larger samples. As the size of samples increases, the number of points in the sampling distribution of F increases; in effect, the discontinuity of the sampling distribution diminishes as sample size increases.

The consequences of small numbers of intervals with small samples have not been thoroughly investigated.   The general attitude among statisticians seems to be that the consequences of discontinuity are negligible, even for rather small samples, when the number of intervals is 20 or more.   When the number of intervals is very small, say five or less, it is certainly advisable to use larger samples.   What combinations of discontinuity and sample size are satisfactory is subject only to arbitrary definition.   We suggest that samples of as few as five units might reasonably be employed when the number of intervals is 20 or more, and that samples of 25 or more subjects probably ought to be used with scales of five units.

To provide the student with some limited evidence as to the actual consequences of a degree of discontinuity encountered fairly often in psychological measurement, a population distribution having five class intervals has been set up.   Frequencies were assigned to the five intervals so that the distribution had a variance of unity and a form approximating that of a normal curve. The histogram for this discrete population distribution is shown in Fig. 8.1.

The true probability of an error of the first kind, corresponding to the nominal 0.05 level of significance for the analysis of variance applied to two samples of two units each from the discrete distribution, was found to be 0.058. The bias is the difference, $(0.058 - 0.050) = 0.008$. In this particular instance, errors of the first kind would occur eight times per thousand more frequently than they should.

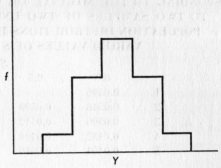

Fig. 8.1 The histogram for a discrete population distribution with unit variance and a form approximating that of a normal curve.

A normal curve is symmetrical and mesokurtic, with values of $S = 0$ and $K = 3$. For asymmetrical curves, S is positive or negative, the sign corresponding to the direction of the skewness. In the case of *platykurtic* or flat distributions, $K < 3$; in the case of *leptokurtic* or peaked curves, $K > 3$.

It can be shown that the effects of skewness and kurtosis diminish as the size of samples increases. When samples are indefinitely large, these departures from normality have no effect on the test of significance. Since one never has indefinitely large samples and must often be satisfied with very small samples, it is of interest to examine these consequences in the case of very small samples. The effects of nonnormality are greatest when the samples are as small as possible and decrease with increases in sample size.

Gayen[6] has investigated the consequences of moderate departures from normality. He employed a generalized, continuous frequency function for the population distribution. In Table 8.1 are the true probabilities for F (based on Gayen's equations) corresponding to the nominal 0.05 probability value for various values of S and K, and samples of two cases each. The nature and extent of the bias can be seen by comparing each entry in the table with 0.05.

When samples are increased in size from two to seven units, the bias is reduced as can be seen in Table 8.2, which is also based on the study by Gayen.[6]

If we examine the probabilities in the rows of Tables 8.1 and 8.2, we see that skewness increases errors of the first kind. If we examine the columns, we see that flatness also increases the number of such errors and that peaked-

Table 8.1
TRUE PROBABILITIES OF ERRORS OF THE FIRST KIND CORRESPONDING TO THE NOMINAL 0.05 VALUE FOR THE *F* TEST APPLIED TO TWO SAMPLES OF TWO UNITS EACH FROM CONTINUOUS POPULATION DISTRIBUTIONS HAVING UNIT VARIANCES AND VARIED VALUES OF *S* AND *K* (From Gayen)

		\(S\) 0.0	0.5	1.0	1.5	2.0
	1	0.0596	—	—	—	—
	2	0.0548	0.0590	0.0632	—	—
K	3	0.0500	0.0542	0.0584	0.0626	0.0668
	4	0.0452	0.0494	0.0536	0.0578	0.0620
	5	0.0404	0.0446	0.0488	0.0530	0.0572

Table 8.2
TRUE PROBABILITIES OF ERRORS OF THE FIRST KIND CORRESPONDING TO THE NOMINAL 0.05 VALUE FOR THE *F* TEST APPLIED TO TWO SAMPLES OF SEVEN UNITS EACH FROM CONTINUOUS POPULATION DISTRIBUTIONS HAVING UNIT VARIANCES AND VARIED VALUES OF *S* AND *K* (From Gayen)

		\(S\) 0.0	0.5	1.0	1.5	2.0
	1	0.0540	—	—	—	—
	2	0.0520	0.0522	0.0524	—	—
K	3	0.0500	0.0502	0.0504	0.0508	0.0510
	4	0.0480	0.0482	0.0486	0.0488	0.0490
	5	0.0460	0.0464	0.0466	0.0468	0.0470

ness reduces their number.   Whenever it is possible, the experimenter should obtain as much information as he can about the nature of the distribution of errors and should take account of the bias introduced by skewness or kurtosis in interpreting his results.   Taking account of the bias would probably mean qualifying his interpretation according to his best judgment about the nature of the bias.

In discussing the theoretical distribution of the *F* ratio, it is sufficient to speak of the population of observations or errors and the frequency function for that population's distribution.   In actual practice, the experimenter is confronted with errors which are not due solely to the selection of materials from a heterogeneous supply.   It has been pointed out several times that differences among subjects are generally recognized as a major source of errors in psychological research.   The experimenter must also allow for errors of measurement and unintended differences that arise from influences beyond his control in the experimental situation. These errors of measurement and unintended differences constitute errors associated with occasions of measurement.

If the differences in the supply of materials and the errors associated with occasions of measurement are, in each case, normally distributed, and if the combining of errors from the two sources is random, then the joint distribution of errors to which the experiment is subject will be normal. Random selection of subjects and random assignment of subjects to treatments and occasions of measurement provide satisfactorily for the combining of the two sources of error. The form of the distribution in each case presents another problem.

Let us defer for a moment consideration of the distribution of errors in the supply of materials and discuss first the errors associated with occasions of measurement. There is nothing the experimenter can do to guarantee, in any absolute sense, that the distribution of errors associated with occasions of measurement will be normal. It is, however, a fact of the experience of scientists in many lines of research that, in a well executed experiment, where care is exercised in making observations and in controlling unintended variation, small errors occur more often than large ones and errors of overestimation occur with no appreciably greater or less frequency than errors of underestimation. The random assignment of these errors over the conditions of the experiment can be expected to generate, in the long run, a symmetrical, unimodal distribution approximating a normal curve. Consequently, there is, in many fields, general acceptance of the idea that careful measurement and good control of the experimental situation will distribute what has traditionally been known as *error* in this fashion.

Situations might arise, of course, in which errors associated with the occasions of measurement would be the result of systematic biases which would certainly not produce normal distributions. For example, if an investigator consistently made several times as many errors of overestimation in measuring as he did errors of underestimation, or if the errors in one direction were considerably larger than errors in the other direction, an asymmetrical distribution would result. In a similar fashion, unintended influences, when subjected to poor control in the course of the experiment, could produce departures from normality in the distribution of errors.

Let us turn now to a consideration of the distribution of inequalities among subjects. The distribution of differences among subjects presents a more serious problem than the distribution of errors associated with occasions of measurement for two reasons. First, no amount of care in obtaining observations has any normalizing effect on the distribution of these errors. Second, there is positive evidence that some response variables are not distributed normally in some populations.

We should point out, however, that it cannot be taken as axiomatic that response variables are not normal, just as it cannot be taken as axiomatic that they are. The form of any distribution is a matter for empirical, not theoretical, determination. The distributions encountered in psychological research do sometimes, although certainly not always, exhibit forms which can be taken as approximations to normal curves. It is not uncommon to find fairly symmetrical distributions possessing a single mode and fewer cases in the tails than in the middle range. Probably the most common departure from normality consists of flatness and a slight skewness.

In theory, it is possible to test an observed distribution of experimental errors for departure from normality. The exact sampling distribution of Fisher's statistics, g_1, a measure of symmetry, and g_2, a measure of kurtosis, are known, thereby making possible tests of significance. For a description of these tests, see Johnson [8] (pp. 151–153).

In actual practice, an observed distribution of errors is seldom tested for departure from normality. The sampling variability of the statistics measuring skewness and kurtosis is quite large for small samples and, consequently, departures from normality would seldom be detected. These tests would find their best application in preliminary, large-sample research whose purpose would be determining the form of the distribution of a given response variable in a specified population.

We take the position here that the consequences of departures from normality, in terms of skewness and kurtosis, usually encountered in practice are not serious for the validity of tests of differences between means when there are ten or more subjects per sample and 20 or more score intervals in the response distribution. When it is known or suspected that the departures from normality in terms of discontinuity, skewness, and kurtosis are extreme, and when the experimenter is limited to the use of very small samples, then the use of a distribution-free or nonparametric statistic is indicated. While the consequences of nonnormality are not usually serious for tests of differences between means, the same cannot be said for tests of the homogeneity of sample variances. The test of homogeneity of variances is quite sensitive to nonnormality.

TRANSFORMATIONS

In some instances, when it is apparent from an inspection of experimental data, or from a test of significance, that the distribution of errors does deviate from normality, it is possible to apply a transformation to the original observations for the purpose of obtaining values which are normally distributed.* There is no certain method of choosing in advance an appropriate transformation. On the basis of theory or prior information as to the nature of the distribution, one may decide to try a particular transformation. If the one selected does not yield the desired results, then another may be tried. In many cases, even when the transformation is the best possible choice, the transformed values will be distributed only approximately as a normal curve.

From a theoretical standpoint, a wide range of nonnormal frequency functions can be normalized. In actual practice, only a few transformations have been found to be useful in normalizing errors in experimental data. Four methods will be described briefly here. These four methods include the logarithmic, square root, angular, and probit transformations.

1. The logarithmic transformation. When the population of observations exhibits positive skewness and sample standard deviations are proportional to sample means, use of the logarithms of experimental observations will tend to normalize the distribution of errors, and make means independent of variances. Mueller[11] has discussed the application of logarithmic transformations to measures of differential thresholds in sensory psychology, to scores for latency of a running response in conditioning, and to the numbers of food pellets hoarded by rats.

2. The square root transformation. In some instances, the positive skewness of the distribution of errors is associated with proportionality of sample variances and means. The skewness and the proportionality can be reduced or eliminated by obtaining the square root of each observation, positive roots only being retained.

3. The angular transformation. When the experimental data consist of proportions, skewness is to be expected if the parametric proportion is close to zero or one. The angular transformation can be used to normalize the distribution. The new values are measures of angles in degrees. The transformation involves finding the angle whose sine is the square root of the original proportion. The procedure is as follows: Find the square root of each proportion. Refer to a table of trigonometric functions. Determine the angle corresponding to a sine value equal to the obtained square root. The analysis of the experiment is then carried out on the angular measures.

---

* Transformations are used for two purposes: (a) to normalize the distribution of errors, and (b) to produce a scale on which treatment effects are additive (see page 80). Of course, we would prefer a transformation which gave both results, but this ideal may not be attainable. A given transformation may yield the one result but not the other.

Tables XII and XIII provided by Fisher and Yates[5] are convenient for converting proportions directly to degrees.

4. The probit transformation.   When reliable normative data are available for a population from which samples will be drawn for experimental purposes, then observations under experimental conditions can be transformed to values normally distributed for the population.   Measures on the population are first converted to centile ranks.   By reference to a table of the normal curve, standard scores can be found corresponding to the centile ranks.   The normalizing process is complete at this point.   For convenience, however, a constant of five units is added to each standard score, thereby eliminating negative values for all practical purposes.   These values have been called *probits*.   When the experimenter obtains his observations, he may refer each one to the normative data and determine the probit corresponding to that observation.   The analysis and evaluation of the experiment are then performed on the transformed values or probits.

Several excellent discussions of the use of transformations are to be found in the literature.   Reference has been made to an article by Mueller.[11] Bartlett,[1] Edwards,[3] Johnson,[8] and Kempthorne[9] also treat the topic.   The interested student will find it profitable to refer to these sources.

CONSEQUENCES OF NONRANDOMNESS

The meaningful application of the theory of statistical inference is critically dependent on satisfaction of the requirement that the errors to which the experiment is liable should be random in their effects.   The problem confronting an investigator is that of finding an appropriate set of operations by means of which the requirement may be fulfilled.   Although a variety of mechanical procedures and devices has been used in the past, the best system presently available employs tables of random numbers that have been tested and found to be satisfactory.

Examination of published research in psychology reveals that the requirement of randomness is often disregarded.   One frequently finds that no attempt has been made by the investigator to insure the randomness of errors. He is content merely to assume that the errors to which his experiment is subject are random.   He does not bother to use tables of random numbers or other equivalent mechanical procedures as guides in the obtaining of observations and in the conduct of the experiment.

It is our viewpoint here that failure to take concrete steps to insure the random distribution of errors is a gross mistake in the conduct of an experiment.   The experimenter has the opportunity to select his materials, to assign them to the conditions of the experiment, and to control the time and place of measurement so that there will be a reasonable expectation that individual differences, errors of measurement, and unintended influences will act as random errors. To forego the opportunity is to leave the experiment subject to a bias whose extent is completely unpredictable in the context of sampling theory. To apply a test of significance to data in these circumstances is a meaningless act, the results of which cannot possibly be trusted.

The issue can be represented by two questions which are implied by the application of any test of significance to experimental data. The first and fundamental question is the following: Is it actually possible that the observed results are the consequence of randomization procedures instituted by the experimenter and carried out under his active management?

The question can and should be answered without reference to or examination of the data. By examining what the experimenter has done in selecting materials, imposing treatments, and obtaining the observations, one can ascertain whether or not randomization procedures have been used. If the randomization was an operational reality, then it is meaningful to ask the second question: What is the probability of obtaining differences as large as or larger than the ones observed, as a consequence of the randomization procedures undertaken by the experimenter?

The answer to the second question is obtained by examination of the sampling distribution of a statistic computed from the experimental observations. The answer makes it possible for the investigator to make a decision as to the outcome of his experiment.

If the answer to the first question is that randomization was not, in fact, instituted by the experimenter, then it is meaningless to ask the second question and no decision based on statistical inference is possible.

The assumption that the errors to which an experiment is subject are random is the most important one of the assumptions discussed in this chapter. The consequences when the other requirements are not fulfilled can be estimated, and allowance can be made for the increase in error. The consequences of nonrandomness are critical. Since, under conditions of nonrandomness, the probability of an error of the first kind is indeterminate, the evaluation of the experiment by statistical inference is invalidated. We should keep in mind that an experiment is a valid experiment in the statistical sense only if the probability of announcing a difference, when there is none, is known and stated by the investigator.

CONSEQUENCES OF A FINITE SUPPLY

The fact that the population distribution in normal curve theory is continuous can be interpreted as implying that the population is infinite in size.

With an infinite population, choices made for one sample do not affect the choices made for any other. In reality, supplies are always finite and sampling is without replacement. To examine the consequences of this failure to meet the requirements, it will be convenient to distinguish, quite arbitrarily, three cases.

1. Although the supply is finite, it is large relative to the samples. By large we mean that the supply is 100 or more times as large as a sample. In this case the bias is negligible, since the correction which might be applied to the standard error of a mean amounts to a reduction of 0.5 per cent of the unadjusted value or less. (See Guilford,[7] pp. 197–198, and McNemar,[10] pp. 99–100.)

2. The sample is a sizable proportion of the supply. We would expect the sampling variation of F ratios to be limited. The probability of errors of the first kind would be reduced. The probability of errors of the second kind would be increased. Although attempts to compensate for this bias are seldom made, one might increase the nominal level of significance by a small amount.

3. The two or more samples required for the experiment exhaust the immediate supply. The available subjects are randomly subdivided into groups and conditions are imposed on them. It makes little or no sense in this case to speak of sampling from a supply. Another way of approaching the problem is to consider the random assignment of subjects to groups as one of a determinable number or population of equally likely arrangements. Special tests of significance, called *randomization tests* and based on the concept of a population of arrangements, have been devised. There is empirical evidence that, under conditions ordinarily encountered in a variety of practical situations, the analysis of variance agrees quite well with the results of randomization tests. Fisher[4] has cited evidence of such a check on the appropriateness of F and t. Welch[12] has also presented evidence of agreement between the analysis of variance and randomization tests.

CONSEQUENCES OF NONADDITIVITY

In designs employing independent samples drawn from the same supply, when the errors are normally distributed and the experimental materials have been randomly assigned to the conditions, constant additive treatment effects will produce homogeneous sample variances within the limits of sampling variability. Nonadditive treatment effects will, in many instances, produce heterogeneous sample variances which may be correlated with sample means. That is to say, when the effect of a given treatment varies from one subject to another, differences due to treatment may affect the estimates of error and bias them. When errors are normally distributed, significant results from the test of homogeneity of sample variances make the assumption of additive treatment effects untenable. It is sometimes possible to find a transformation which will yield a scale on which effects are additive and means are independent of variances.

Even though the finding of heterogeneous sample variances creates a problem in the evaluation of differences among sample means, we should not overlook the information or lightly discard it. Many investigators have directed their interest to differences among means and have paid little attention to evidence of differences among variances produced by treatments. Detecting differences among variances can conceivably be important in its own right, without regard for the differences among means.

One precaution of interpretation should be noted. Finding significant differences among sample variances is not always indicative of nonadditive treatment effects. When errors are not distributed normally, sample means and variances will not be independent and the test of homogeneity of variances will be affected. A transformation will often tend to equalize the variances as well as normalize the errors. In such cases, a double advantage accrues from the transformation, and circumstances are more favorable for the evaluation of the experiment.

Having found heterogeneous sample variances, however, the investigator may still wish to proceed with his evaluation of the differences among means with the hope that the consequences of heterogeneity will not completely invalidate his work. Let us examine the consequences of heterogeneity of sample variances in the evaluation of differences among means.

Welch[13] investigated the probability associated with the F test of the difference between sample means when the variances of the two populations from which the samples came were unequal. When the samples were of equal size, ten units in each, Welch found that the true probability of an error of the first kind corresponding to the nominal 0.05 level of significance lay between 0.050 and 0.065 as the ratio of one population variance to the other varied from 0.01 to 100. When the samples were of unequal sizes, the test was subject to greater bias.

David and Johnson[2] did a similar study of the effects of unequal population variances on the comparison of the between-sample variability and the within-sample variability. Three normal populations with equal means and unequal variances were used. The magnitudes of the three population variances were, respectively, 1, 2, and 3. The true probability of an error of the first kind was determined for seven combinations of four samples of six units each. Each combination of four samples included one or more samples from one or more of the populations. The populations from which the samples for each combination came are indicated in Table 8.3 by the combination of values representing population variances. The true probabilities corresponding to the nominal 0.05 value are also given.

Table 8.3
TRUE PROBABILITIES OF ERRORS OF THE FIRST KIND FOR THE ANALYSIS OF VARIANCE ON COMBINATIONS OF FOUR SAMPLES FROM THREE NORMAL POPULATIONS HAVING UNEQUAL VARIANCES
(From David and Johnson)

					P_t
	1	1	1	1	0.050
Combinations	1	1	1	2	0.057
of populations	1	1	2	2	0.057
in terms of	1	2	2	2	0.055
variances	1	1	1	3	0.063
	1	1	2	3	0.060
	1	1	3	3	0.063

Sample size: $n = 6$
P_t = the true probability

We observe from both studies that heterogeneity of sample variances increases the probability of errors of the first kind in the test of significance for differences between means.

POWER

Validity has to do with errors of the first kind; power has to do with errors of the second kind. Validity is a primary goal of the experimenter. Its principal guarantee is randomization. Given randomization, validity can always be increased by increasing the size of samples. Power, too, is a goal of the experimenter. Given random errors, power can be increased in three ways: (a) by increasing the magnitude of the treatment effect, (b) by increasing the size of samples, and (c) by reducing the size of errors.

Increasing the magnitude of the treatment effect is sometimes possible, but not always. The choice of the particular qualities or levels of treatment for an experiment might be made with a view to producing the largest possible effects. Larger effects would be detectable more often.

Increasing the size of samples is often a good possibility for increasing power. The effect is to reduce the sampling variability of the F ratio, thereby allowing treatment effects of some given magnitude to be detected more often. There are many occasions, of course, when the experimenter cannot obtain or cannot afford large samples.

Reducing the size of errors affecting the experiment is an elegant and very effective way of increasing the power of a test. It is fundamental. It is in the best traditions of science and the quest for knowledge. Reducing the size of errors is often termed *increasing the precision* of a design. Precision and the methods for increasing it constitute the next important topic in our discussion. It will be taken up in Chapter 9.

ADDED COMMENTS ON THE SUPPLY

To conduct an experiment, the investigator must secure experimental materials from an available supply. In psychological research, he must obtain human or animal subjects from an accessible group of subjects. What bearing does the selection of materials have on the interpretation of the results of the experiment? Any conclusions as to the nature of the materials to which the results of a given experiment are applicable are dictated by the experimenter's choice of a supply. Results cannot be discussed without regard for the nature of the materials used. The results of a given experiment are meaningless until the experimenter can say to what class of materials the results apply. In reporting and interpreting his results, the experimenter should specify quite clearly the characteristics of the supply of materials from which he has made his selection.

When the subjects in an experiment are randomly selected from a larger supply, the attempt to generalize the results of the experiment to that supply is subject to a known and stated error. The generalization to the supply takes place in the context of statistical inference. When the population is a population of arrangements rather than materials, generalization of the results to other collections of materials can only be achieved on a common-sense basis. That is to say, the experimenter must rely on his own judgment as to the nature of the materials to which the results apply. Generalization is not supported by the formal procedures of statistical inference.

The specification of the supply serves another important purpose. It makes possible the repetition or *replication* of the experiment with the results of replications subject to predictable variation. Since the results of any single experiment, no matter how small the probability associated with the observed results is, could be the result of errors, replication of an experiment is essential. If the supply of materials is not specified, the experiment cannot, in a strict sense, be replicated. The same treatments can be applied to different materials, but the result will be a new experiment, not a replication of the original one. Specifying the supply in research reports is especially important in that independent investigators in other laboratories can then employ approximately equivalent materials, repeat the experiment, and verify the results.

When the population is a population of arrangements rather than materials, replication of a given experiment, in the sense implied by the definition, cannot be carried out. If the concept of a population of arrangements is adopted, a single replication would require repetition of the experiment with another random arrangement of the same subjects.   Using the same subjects in a replication is rarely possible in psychological research, because of the changes produced in the subjects on the first occasion.   Replication in a practical sense will likely involve the use of groups of subjects judged to be similar to the subjects in the original experiment.   The procedure is not ideal. What the consequences are cannot be stated in general terms.   The consequences in many instances are probably not serious; in other instances, the intended replications may not be replications at all.   Unfortunately the experimenter may have no way of knowing what the real situation is.

REFERENCES

1. Bartlett, M. S., "The Use of Transformations," *Biometrics*, 3, 1947, 39-52.
2. David, F. N. and Johnson, N. L., "The Effect of Nonnormality on the Power Function of the *F* Test in the Analysis of Variance," *Biometrika*, 38, 1951, 43-57.
3. Edwards, A. L., *Experimental Design in Psychological Research*. New York: Rinehart & Co., Inc., 1950.
4. Fisher, R. A., *The Design of Experiments*.   New York: Hafner Publishing Co., 1949.
5. Fisher, R. A. and Yates, F., *Statistical Tables for Biological, Agricultural and Medical Research*.   Edinburgh: Oliver & Boyd, Ltd., 1943.
6. Gayen, A. K., "Significance of a Difference Between the Means of Two Non-normal Samples," *Biometrika*, 37, 1950, 399-408.
7. Guilford, J. P., *Fundamental Statistics in Psychology and Education*.   New York: McGraw-Hill Book Co., 1956.
8. Johnson, P. O., *Statistical Methods in Research*.   New York: Prentice-Hall, Inc., 1949.
9. Kempthorne, O., *The Design and Analysis of Experiments*.   New York: John Wiley & Sons, Inc., 1952.
10. McNemar, Q., *Psychological Statistics*.   New York: John Wiley & Sons, Inc., 1955.
11. Mueller, C. G., "Numerical Transformations in the Analysis of Experimental Data," *Psychological Bulletin*, 46, 1949, 198-223.
12. Welch, B. L., "On the *Z* Test in Randomized Blocks and Latin Squares," *Biometrika*, 29, 1937, 21-52.
13. Welch, B. L., "The Significance of the Difference Between Two Means When the Population Variances are Unequal," *Biometrika*, 29, 1938, 350-362.

MATCHING

9

Since the presence of error in the scientist's observations is inevitable, his knowledge of any phenomenon is always partial and incomplete. To a considerable extent, his efforts to acquire new knowledge take the form of attempts to reduce the error in the basic observations on which knowledge ultimately depends. Two kinds of erroneous decisions in evaluating experiments have been identified. When the assumptions underlying the test of significance have been met satisfactorily, the probability of rejecting the null hypothesis when it should be accepted is determined by the experimenter's choice of a level of significance. The probability of accepting the null hypothesis when it should be rejected depends, in part, upon the magnitude of errors in the experiment. Reducing the size of errors decreases the probability of an error of the second kind and increases the power of the test of significance. Reducing the size of errors is also described as increasing the *precision* of the design.

The single-variable experiment with independent random samples provides a valid test of significance. In psychological research, however, it is not a very useful design. Because of the extreme heterogeneity of experimental materials in psychological experimentation, a design employing small random samples with no attempt to reduce the influence of heterogeneous materials will be subject to large errors; that is, it will be lacking in precision. Under these circumstances, small treatment differences will seldom be detected. If relatively large samples are employed or if quite large treatment effects are produced, then the power of the test of significance may, of course, be quite satisfactory.

There is a logical solution to the problem of reducing the influence of heterogeneous materials on experimental results. In a single-variable experiment involving two conditions, the experimenter should choose two subjects who, prior to the experiment, give evidence of being exactly comparable. The selection of exactly comparable subjects is, obviously, impossible. The selection of two subjects who are very much alike is often possible, however, and it is this kind of selection or *matching* which provides a practical solution to the problem of heterogeneity.

The experimenter selects two subjects who are very much alike with respect to the characteristics of the response being studied in the experiment. One condition is imposed on the first subject; the other condition is imposed on the second subject. Measurements of response are made. A comparison of the two measures can then be undertaken. It is quite likely that the comparison is biased, since it is very unlikely that the two subjects have been matched without error. If the selection or matching is effective in yielding two subjects very much alike, then the error will be smaller than it would have been with no attempt at matching.

To obtain some idea of the magnitude of the error that still remains in the comparison, the experimenter must repeat his selection of a pair of subjects and the imposition of treatments. The members of each pair are matched; that is, they are chosen to be as much alike as possible. One condition is then imposed on one member of each pair. A second condition is imposed on the other member. The assignment of subjects to conditions should be random within each pair. Finally, a measure of response is obtained on each subject.

The experimenter can now compare the two conditions as many times as there are matched pairs. He can make the comparisons by computing a difference for each pair. The differences may vary in direction and magnitude, being positive or negative, large or small. Averaging these differences gives him the apparent difference between the treatments. When the assignment of conditions to the subjects within each pair has been done randomly, and when the treatment effects are constant and additive, the variability of the differences will reflect the magnitude of errors arising from failures in matching.

That the errors can be gauged in this way is explained as follows. Suppose that the differential effect of the two conditions was the same on every pair and that the members of each pair were matched perfectly. Then the differences obtained would be identical and would exhibit no variability. The experimenter would conclude, and correctly so, that there were no errors in the experiment. If the members of each pair were not matched perfectly, however, and the direction of influence of the failure in matching had been randomly determined in each case, then the differences would vary. The poorer the matching, the more variable these differences would be. Thus there is available, in the variability of the collection of differences, information concerning the magnitude of the errors affecting the experiment.

When the apparent treatment differences are large relative to the variability of the differences, the experimenter will have greater confidence that the treatments have actually produced differences. When the apparent treatment differences are small relative to the variability of the differences, the experimenter will suspect that the treatments have not really had different effects and that the apparent treatment effects are due to errors.

As in the case of the design that involved no matching, the experimenter needs a plan for conducting the experiment in a manner that makes it possible for him to compare the apparent treatment effects with an estimate of the errors which may have produced them. He also needs a systematic procedure for making a decision as to the results of the comparison.

The variability in data from matched pairs can be analyzed. Components of variability can be compared. With a proper design, a component of variability which includes the effects of treatments and a component that represents error can be identified. Finally, a valid test of significance is available for the comparison of the two sources of variability.

THE ANALYSIS OF VARIABILITY

Consider the numbers in Table 9.1. The ten numbers have been classified into five rows, labeled with Arabic numerals, and two columns, labeled with Roman numerals.

Table 9.1
A CLASSIFICATION OF NUMBERS BY ROWS AND COLUMNS

	Columns	
	I	II
1	3	7
2	5	9
Rows 3	1	5
4	4	6
5	2	8

The total variability in the entire table is measured by the total sum of squares, which is equal to 60.

Let us eliminate the variability in each column by substituting the mean of column I for each number in that column and the mean of column II for each number in that column. Table 9.2 gives the results of the substitutions. Notice that the variability in each column has been eliminated, that there are

Table 9.2

THE CLASSIFICATION AFTER ELIMINATION OF THE COLUMN VARIABILITY IN TABLE 9.1

		Columns	
		I	II
	1	3	7
	2	3	7
Rows	3	3	7
	4	3	7
	5	3	7

no differences within a column. Some variability does remain in the entire set, however. The remaining variability can be described as differences between columns. The sum of squares for the ten values as they appear in Table 9.2 is 40. In other words, the between-column sum of squares is equal to 40.

Let us return to the original numbers in Table 9.1 and eliminate the variability in each row by substituting the mean of a given row for each value in that row. Table 9.3 gives the results of the substitution. Within-row variability has been eliminated. Some variability does remain, however, and it can be described as differences between rows. The sum of squares for the ten values in Table 9.3 is 16. Thus the between-row sum of squares is equal to 16.

Table 9.3

**THE CLASSIFICATION AFTER ELIMINATION OF
THE ROW VARIABILITY IN TABLE 9.1**

Columns

		I	II
	1	5	5
	2	7	7
Rows	3	3	3
	4	5	5
	5	5	5

Recall that the total sum of squares for the original values in Table 9.1 is 60. The between-column sum of squares is 40. The between-row sum of squares is 16. The two components do not combine to give the total. This fact suggests that another component can be identified. This third component, which is usually referred to as *residual* variablity, can be obtained by subtracting the other two components from the total. The subtraction

$$60 - 40 - 16 = 4$$

shows that the residual sum of squares is 4. It can also be computed independently.

To illustrate its independent computation, we begin with the following equation as a definition of r, a residual deviation:

$$r_{jk} = (Y_{jk} - \bar{Y}_{..}) - (\bar{Y}_{j.} - \bar{Y}_{..}) - (\bar{Y}_{.k} - \bar{Y}_{..}),$$

which says that a residual deviation is what remains of the deviation from the total mean after deviations of the row and column means have been removed. The right member can be simplified, by combining terms to yield

$$r_{jk} = (Y_{jk} - \bar{Y}_{j.} - \bar{Y}_{.k} + \bar{Y}..),\tag{9.1}$$

where the symbols are defined as follows:

r_{jk} = the residual for the cell in the jth row and kth column,

Y_{jk} = the original value for the cell in the jth row and kth column,

$\bar{Y}_{j.}$ = the mean of the jth row,

$\bar{Y}_{.k}$ = the mean of the kth column,

$\bar{Y}..$ = the mean of the entire set, or the total mean.

The residual for the cell in the first row and first column, r_{11}, is computed in the following manner:

$$r_{11} = 3 - 5 - 3 + 5 = 0.$$

Residuals for the other cells have been computed in a similar fashion and are displayed in Table 9.4.

Table 9.4
RESIDUALS FOR THE CLASSIFICATION IN TABLE 9.1

		Columns	
		I	II
	1	0	0
	2	0	0
Rows	3	0	0
	4	+1	−1
	5	−1	+1

The variability of the residuals can be measured. Since their mean is always zero, the residuals themselves are deviations which can be squared and summed over the entire set. The sum of squares of the residuals in Table 9.4 is 4, exactly the quantity determined previously by subtracting two components from the total. This example demonstrates the fact that the total sum of squares can be subdivided into three additive components, the between-column sum of squares, the between-row sum of squares, and the residual sum of squares. In the example,

$$60 = 40 + 16 + 4.$$

The analysis which has just been applied to Table 9.1 can be applied to any rectangular table of r rows and c columns when there is one value per cell. The total variability for such a table is, in general, equal to the sum of the three components: the between-column, the between-row, and the residual sums of squares. No proof of this general relation will be presented here.

FORMULAS

Computing formulas will now be given and applied to the classification of numbers given in Table 9.1.

The formula for the total sum of squares, formula (4.2), was

$$\Sigma Y^2 - C'$$

The summary data required are:

$$\Sigma Y = 50,$$
$$(\Sigma Y)^2 = 2500,$$
$$C' = (\Sigma Y)^2/N = 2500/10 = 250,$$
$$\Sigma Y^2 = 310.$$

The computation of the total sum of squares:

$$310 - 250 = 60$$

The formula for the between-column sum of squares, adapted from formula (4.3), is

$$\frac{\sum_k \left(\sum_j Y_{jk} \right)^2}{r} - C'.$$

The summary data required are:

$$\sum_j Y_{j1} = \text{the sum of column I} = 15,$$

$$\sum_j Y_{j2} = \text{the sum of column II} = 35,$$

$$\left(\sum_j Y_{j1}\right)^2 = 15^2 = 225,$$

$$\left(\sum_j Y_{j2}\right)^2 = 35^2 = 1225,$$

$$r = 5,$$

$$C' = 250.$$

Computation of the between-column sum of squares:

$$\frac{225 + 1225}{5} - 250 = 40.$$

The formula for the between-row sum of squares, adapted from formula (4.3), is

$$\frac{\sum_j \left(\sum_k Y_{jk}\right)^2}{c} - C'.$$

The summary data required are:

$$\sum_k Y_{1k} = \text{the sum of row 1} = 10,$$

$$\sum_k Y_{2k} = \text{the sum of row 2} = 14,$$

$$\sum_k Y_{3k} = 6,$$

$$\sum_k Y_{4k} = 10,$$

$$\sum_k Y_{5k} = 10,$$

$$c = 2,$$

$$C' = 250.$$

Computation of the between-row sum of squares:

$$\frac{10^2 + 14^2 + 6^2 + 10^2 + 10^2}{2} - 250 = 16.$$

The formula for a residual deviation, formula (9.1), is

$$r_{jk} = (Y_{jk} - \bar{Y}_{j.} - \bar{Y}_{.k} + \bar{Y}_{..}).$$

The summary data required for all cells are:

$$r_{11} = 3 - 5 - 3 + 5 = 0,$$
$$r_{21} = 5 - 7 - 3 + 5 = 0,$$
$$r_{31} = 1 - 3 - 3 + 5 = 0,$$
$$r_{41} = 4 - 5 - 3 + 5 = +1,$$
$$r_{51} = 2 - 5 - 3 + 5 = -1,$$
$$r_{12} = 7 - 5 - 7 + 5 = 0,$$
$$r_{22} = 9 - 7 - 7 + 5 = 0,$$
$$r_{32} = 5 - 3 - 7 + 5 = 0,$$
$$r_{42} = 6 - 5 - 7 + 5 = -1,$$
$$r_{52} = 8 - 5 - 7 + 5 = +1.$$

Computation of the residual sum of squares:

$$0^2 + 0^2 + 0^2 + 1^2 + (-1)^2 + 0^2 + 0^2 + 0^2 + (-1)^2 + 1^2 = 4.$$

THEORY

The sampling model calls for r normally distributed populations. The r populations have equal variances, but may or may not have equal means. From each of the populations, c observations are randomly drawn and tabulated, in the random order of their occurrence, one per cell in a row of a table having c columns and r rows. The cells of a row will then contain c observations from one of the r populations.

The variability in the table of r rows and c columns can be analyzed, and three components of variability can be identified. These include the between-column sum of squares, the between-row sum of squares, and the residual sum of squares. An unbiased estimate of the common population variance can be computed by dividing the between-column sum of squares by $(c - 1)$ degrees of freedom. An unbiased estimate of the common population variance can be computed by dividing the residual sum of squares by $(r - 1)(c - 1)$ degrees of freedom. Since the population means may differ, the between-row component cannot be used as an estimate.

The between-column variance can be compared with the residual variance in an F ratio and the sampling distribution of F has been determined. That is to say, the totality of comparison outcomes is known. By referring to the appropriate F function, it is possible to ascertain the probability associated with a value of the ratio.

PRACTICE

The uniformity trial by which the investigator may attempt to implement statistical theory in using matched pairs of subjects involves the following operations.

A supply of materials is specified and enumerated. A random sample of materials is obtained. A response variable of interest to the investigator is selected as the dependent variable. Another response variable that is known to be correlated with the dependent variable is selected as a *matching* variable.

Subjects are measured under uniform conditions on the matching variable. They are next ranked according to the magnitude of the matching measures. The first and second individuals in the ranking are selected for the first matched pair. The third and fourth individuals are selected for the second matched pair. The matching into pairs is continued in the same manner until the sample is exhausted. In proportion to the magnitude of the correlation between the matching variable and the dependent variable, selection on the matching variable will result in selection on the dependent variable. Matching of pairs on the dependent variable is thus indirectly achieved.

The members of each pair are now assigned randomly to two groups, I and II, and then to two occasions of measurement. Subjects are then measured under uniform conditions on the dependent variable. The resulting measures can be classified in a table of two columns, I and II, corresponding to the two random groupings, and a number of rows, corresponding to the matched pairs.

If an investigator actually carried out the procedures of the uniformity trial outlined above, he would obtain a table of measures possessing variability. The variability could be analyzed into three components. The between-column sum of squares would represent the differences between groups I and II, which differences would actually be a consequence of the random assignment of the members of each pair to a group. The between-row sum of squares would represent differences among the pairs produced by the matching. The magnitude of the between-row component is determined by the effectiveness of the matching and is not subject to the influence of the randomization. The difference between any two pairs would not be changed by a different random arrangement of the members in either pair. The residual sum of squares would represent the variability of the pair differences and would be influenced by the randomization.

The between-column variance and the residual variance can be computed and can be compared in an F ratio, the between-column variance over the residual variance.

THE FORMAL EXPERIMENT

Consider how the matched-pair design would be implemented in an experiment having a single independent variable consisting of the two conditions, A and B. The investigator obtains a random sample of experimental materials from the supply. The subjects in the sample are measured under uniform conditions on the matching variable. The subjects are next ranked and then arranged in pairs in the manner previously described for the uniformity trial. The members of each pair are assigned randomly to the two conditions, A and B, and to certain occasions of measurement. Conditions are imposed. Measurements on the dependent variable are obtained and tabulated, as shown in Table 9.5.

Table 9.5
ARRANGEMENT OF CONDITIONS, SUBJECTS, AND OBSERVATIONS FOR A SINGLE-VARIABLE, MATCHED-PAIR DESIGN

	Conditions	
	A	B
1	Y_{11}	Y_{12}
2	Y_{21}	Y_{22}
3	Y_{31}	Y_{32}
Pairs of Subjects ·	·	·
j	Y_{j1}	Y_{j2}
·	·	·
r	Y_{r1}	Y_{r2}

Let us consider the variability in the experimental data. We shall want to identify two components. One component, which is to be evaluated, should contain error and treatment effects. The other, which serves as a standard and makes the evaluation possible, should contain only error.

The total variability in the experimental data will contain differences produced by the matching, differences due to uncontrolled influences and failures in matching, and treatment effects.

Differences produced by matching are contained in the between-row component. This component will be large when the matching is effective, and is of no special interest to the experimenter. It is usually computed to provide a check on the computation of the other components but no further use is made of it.

It is instructive to examine the relation between the experimental comparisons, which are to be evaluated, and the differences between the rows or the matched pairs. The differences between pairs do not need to be considered in evaluating the experiment. Each row, or each pair, provides a comparison of the two treatments, *A* and *B*. Since each comparison of the two treatments can be limited to the two subjects in a matched pair, the error in each comparison comes from the failure in matching and is not in any way dependent on the difference between that pair and any other. The influence of differences between pairs is therefore eliminated from the physical experiment, and the corresponding variability ought to be eliminated in the statistical analysis. Through the matching procedure, the experimenter endeavors to maximize the differences between pairs and to minimize the differences within pairs, and, having done so to the best of his ability, he sets aside the between-row component as being of no further interest.

In being randomly distributed over the conditions, failures in matching and errors associated with occasions of measurement will have combined to introduce a bias in the between-column component. When the treatment effects are constant and additive, they will also be contained in, and, as a matter of fact, limited to the between-column component. Additive effects will not enter the between-row or residual variability.

It is a simple matter to demonstrate that constant additive effects change only the total and the between-column sums of squares, and do not at all influence the other two components. Let us use for demonstration purposes the numbers classified by row and column in Table 9.1. The total sum of squares, as determined by the previous analysis, is 60. The between-column sum of squares is 40; the between-row component is 16; the residual is 4. Now add a constant of one unit to each number in the second column. The total sum of squares is increased to 82.5. The between-column component is increased by an equivalent amount to 62.5. The other components are unchanged. The student can check these results by his own computation.

Notice that, in the experiment as in the uniformity trial, the differences between columns are subject to the influence of randomization. Any different arrangement of members within pairs would likely result in a change in the measures in any column and a consequent change in the differences between columns. It is therefore possible to say that, when the treatments have had no effect, the differences between columns have actually been produced by the randomization. Since the between-column component contains both treatment effects and error, it must be evaluated.

We observed, in the simple numerical example above, that constant additive treatment effects do not influence the residual sum of squares. The residual variability is, however, influenced by the randomization. A different arrangement of subjects within pairs would likely produce a different set of residuals. Since the residual variability is affected by randomization and does not change with constant additive treatment effects, it can be said to contain nothing but error.

The magnitude of the residual variability is, on the average, a function of the magnitude of the differences within pairs arising from the inadequacies of the matching and the disparities among the occasions of measurement. That is to say, the poorer the matching, the larger the residual variability will be, on the average, over many repetitions of the experiment. It follows that an estimate of the error variance, a measure of the errors to which the experiment is liable, can be computed from the residual sum of squares. The greater the residual variability, the more suspect the apparent treatment differences are. The smaller the residual variability, the more confidence the experimenter can have that the treatment differences are real.

The experimenter compares the apparent treatment effects, as measured by the between-column variance, with the estimate of error, as given by the residual variance, in an F ratio. The between-column variance is computed by dividing its sum of squares by one degree of freedom. The residual variance is computed with $(r - 1)$ degrees of freedom. If his obtained F is greater than the criterion F, he rejects the null hypothesis. If it is smaller, he accepts the null hypothesis.

When the treatment effects are not constant and additive, the residual component will be biased and the estimate of error will be biased. In designs employing independent random samples, a test of homogeneity of sample variances is applied to determine whether or not the assumption that treatment effects are constant and additive is justified. In the design employing matched pairs, no test of additivity is commonly used, although there is one available, devised by Tukey.[4]

AN ALTERNATIVE METHOD OF EVALUATION

The t ratio is also appropriate for evaluating the matched-pair design. The formula for the ratio is

$$t = (\sqrt{r}) \frac{\bar{D}}{S_d},$$

where r is the number of pairs, $\bar{D}$ is the average of the r differences, and S_d is the standard deviation of the differences computed with $(r - 1)$ degrees of freedom. The t ratio compares $\bar{D}$, the average difference and apparent effect of the treatments, with S_d, a measure of the variability of the differences and an estimate of error. In the matched-pair design, $t^2 = F$.

MORE THAN TWO CONDITIONS

The simplest form of the matching design involves two conditions and experimental materials arranged in matched pairs. The design can be enlarged to include any number of conditions for the independent variable. The several conditions may differ among themselves qualitatively or quantitatively. When the number of conditions is greater than two, subjects are not matched in pairs. The size of the matched group corresponds to the number of conditions. With three conditions, subjects would be matched in triplets. With four conditions, they would be matched in quadruplets. Designs employing matched groups of experimental materials are generally known in other fields as *randomized block designs*. The general form of the analysis is given in Table 9.6.

Table 9.6
GENERAL FORM OF THE ANALYSIS OF VARIANCE
FOR A MATCHED-GROUP DESIGN

Component	df	V	F
Treatments	$c - 1$	V_t	V_t/V_e
Matched groups	$r - 1$		
Residual error	$(r - 1)(c - 1)$	V_e	
Total	$N - 1$		

c = number of conditions
r = number of matched groups
$N = rc$ = total number of subjects

Instead of matching groups himself, the psychologist can sometimes use natural groupings. For example, litters of animals may serve the purpose of matched groups. In general, the value of natural groupings in increasing the precision of an experiment in psychological research is limited. The limitation derives from the fact that differences within a group—a litter, for example—are usually substantial. Use of an effective matching variable instead of the natural groups would insure the elimination of a large proportion of the individual variation.

AN EXAMPLE

A psychologist was interested in determining the effect of monetary rewards of varying amounts on the performance of young boys on a perceptual-motor task. The task chosen was a dart game that could be scored according to the accuracy of the individual's throws. Three levels of reward were used. The first level involved no reward; the second involved a reward of one dollar; the third, a reward of two dollars.

Twenty-four boys were selected randomly from the seventh grade of a junior high schol. The boys were tested prior to the experiment on the dart game. On the basis of their pretest scores, they were ranked and placed in eight matched groups of three boys each. Within each matched group, the three boys were assigned randomly to the three levels of reward.

In conducting the experiment, the investigator tested each boy individually. At the time of testing, the boy was urged to do his best on the task and, if he was to receive a reward, he was so informed. The 24 boys were tested in a random order for the three boys in each of the eight groups. The scores constituting the dependent variable are given in Table 9.7. The analysis is presented below.

Table 9.7
DATA FROM AN EXPERIMENT EMPLOYING MATCHED GROUPS

		Reward Conditions		
		Level 1	Level 2	Level 3
	1	31	20	21
	2	29	25	24
	3	27	29	28
Matched	4	24	29	31
Groups	5	13	36	41
	6	21	37	44
	7	25	35	42
	8	30	37	41

The formula for the total sum of squares, formula (4.2), is

$$\Sigma Y^2 - C'$$

Summary data:

$$\Sigma Y = 720,$$
$$(\Sigma Y)^2 = 518,400,$$
$$N = 24,$$
$$C' = (\Sigma Y)^2 / N = 518,400/24 = 21,600,$$
$$\Sigma Y^2 = 23,032.$$

Computation of the total sum of squares:

$$23,032 - 21,600 = 1432.$$

The formula for the between-column sum of squares, adapted from formula (4.3), is

$$\frac{\sum_k \left(\sum_j Y_{jk} \right)^2}{r} - C'.$$

Summary data:

$$\sum_j Y_{j1} = 200, \qquad \left(\sum_j Y_{j1} \right)^2 = 40,000,$$

$$\sum_j Y_{j2} = 248, \qquad \left(\sum_j Y_{j2} \right)^2 = 61,504,$$

$$\sum_j Y_{j3} = 272, \qquad \left(\sum_j Y_{j3} \right)^2 = 73,984,$$

$$r = 8,$$

$$C' = 21,600.$$

Computation of the between-column sum of squares:

$$(40,000 + 61,504 + 73,984)/8 - 21,600 = 336.$$

The formula for the between-row sum of squares, adapted from formula (4.3), is

$$\frac{\sum_j \left(\sum_k Y_{jk} \right)^2}{c} - C'.$$

Summary data:

The row sums and squared sums are listed below:

72	5184
78	6084
84	7056
84	7056
90	8100
102	10,404
102	10,404
108	11,664

$$c = 3,$$
$$C' = 21,600.$$

Computation of the between-row sum of squares:

$$(5184 + 6084 + 7056 + 7056 + 8100 + 10,404 + 10,404 + 11,664)/3$$
$$- 21,600 = 384.$$

The formula for a residual deviation, formula (9.1), is

$$r_{jk} = Y_{jk} - \bar{Y}_{j.} - \bar{Y}_{.k} + \bar{Y}_{...}$$

Summary data: The residual deviations are given in Table 9.8; the sum of the squares of these residuals is 712.

Table 9.8
RESIDUAL DEVIATIONS FOR THE MATCHED-GROUP DATA IN TABLE 9.7

		Reward Conditions		
		Level 1	Level 2	Level 3
	1	12	−5	−7
	2	8	−2	−6
	3	4	0	−4
Matched	4	1	0	−1
Groups	5	−12	5	7
	6	−8	2	6
	7	−4	0	4
	8	−1	0	1

A check on the computation: The total sum of squares should equal the sum of the three components. We observe that

$$1432 = 336 + 384 + 712.$$

The computation checks.

The treatment variance, V_t, is computed by dividing the between-column sum of squares, 336, by $(c - 1) = 2$ degrees of freedom. That is,

$$V_t = \frac{336}{2} = 168.$$

The error variance, V_e, is computed by dividing the residual sum of squares, 712, by $(r - 1)(c - 1) = (7)(2) = 14$ degrees of freedom. Then

$$V_e = \frac{712}{14} = 50.86.$$

F is the ratio of the treatment variance to the error variance. Therefore

$$F = \frac{168}{50.86} = 3.30.$$

The criterion value of F for the .05 level of significance and the combination of degrees of freedom, 2 and 14, is 3.74. The null hypothesis is accepted. The results are presented in the conventional manner in Table 9.9.

Table 9.9
ANALYSIS OF VARIANCE OF DATA IN TABLE 9.7
FOR A MATCHED-GROUP DESIGN

Component of variability	SS	df	V	F	F_c
Between levels of reward	336	2	168	3.30*	3.74
Between matched groups	384	7			
Residual or error	712	14	50.86		
Total	1432	23			

* $F < F_c$; Null hypothesis accepted.

ERRORS OF THE FIRST AND SECOND KINDS

When the requirements of normal curve theory are fulfilled, the analysis of variance provides a valid test of significance for the matched-group design. Pitman[3] and Welch [5] have shown that the analysis of variance gives approximately the same results as the randomization test when the group variances are homogeneous or nearly so. No assumption about the form of the distribution of errors is necessary. In the randomization test, the obtained arrangement of observations is compared with the totality of arrangements that are possible as outcomes of the random assignment of subjects within each group to the conditions.

The advantage of the matched-group design is found in the reduction of the probability of errors of the second kind. Since effective matching will result in a smaller error in each comparison that might otherwise occur, the precision of the experiment will be increased. Small treatment differences will be detected more frequently. Significant results will more often be announced when they should be.

The extent to which errors of the second kind are reduced will vary widely from one situation to another. The increase in precision will be a function of the correlation between the matching variable and the dependent variable. The most effective matching would be achieved when there is a perfect correlation between the two variables and the number of matched groups is very large. With a small number of subjects and groups, the matching would rarely, if ever, be perfect, even if the correlation was very high, for differences among subjects within each group would not be eliminated.

The effectiveness of the matched-group design is also a function of the total number of subjects used and the size of the matched groups. For a total sample of a given size, the differences within a group will increase in magnitude, and errors of the second kind will increase in frequency as the size of the matched group increases. Consequently, the reduction of errors will be greatest for designs involving matched pairs.

When the size of the matched group is fixed, errors of the second kind will decrease in frequency with increases in the size of the total sample. The differences within each matched group will be smaller as the total sample is enlarged. In addition, with a larger number of replications, the number of degrees of freedom available for an estimate of error will increase. We have already seen that power is a function of the number of observations.

SUMMARY

The matched group design offers possibilities for increasing the precision of an experiment. The underlying principle of the design is that each set of experimental comparisons is made on a group of subjects exhibiting as much homogeneity as the experimenter can possibly achieve. In conducting such an experiment, the investigator must examine his materials and then actually arrange them into homogeneous groupings. One disadvantage of the matched-group design is that the matching procedure ordinarily requires a lapse of time between measurement on the matching variable and the actual conduct of the experiment. The lapse of time is needed for the ranking, grouping, and random assigning of subjects. This lapse of time may force the psychologist to make additional appointments with his subjects. It will also very likely reduce the final effectiveness of the matching. As far as the experiment is concerned, the best matching would be achieved immediately after the preliminary measurement.

REPEATED TREATMENT

It is sometimes possible and desirable to use the same subjects in two or more different conditions, in which case a measure on each subject is obtained under each condition. A tempting feature of such a design is the advantage of reducing errors by making each set of desired comparisons on a single subject and thus eliminating differences among individuals. In some instances, however, the advantage may only be apparent and not real, for biases of other kinds can be incurred.

Before adopting a design in which each subject appears in all of the conditions, the investigator should first satisfy himself that repeated measurement on the dependent variable is feasible. If an initial measurement on the dependent variable precludes further measurement on that variable, the design obviously cannot be used. The investigator should next consider the problems created by what are often referred to as *order effects*. If the effect of a given treatment on a subject depends on the effect of the treatment or treatments that preceded it, then the order in which treatments are imposed will affect the experimental observations and must be taken account of in the planning and again in the evaluation of the experiment.

Consider first the situation in which the effects of the order of imposing treatments are negligible. Negligible order effects are often encountered by the psychologist in studies of visual and auditory discriminations. The effect of any one of the several conditions in a given experiment on visual or auditory thresholds may be temporary, so that the several effects may be independent or nearly so.

When the same subjects appear in all conditions and when the order effects are negligible, then the errors affecting the comparisons can be described, in general terms, as errors associated with the occasions of measurement. These errors will be the combined or net effects of errors of measurement, unintended or extraneous influences, and fluctuations in the responses of subjects due to interest, fatigue, adaptation, learning, etc. The fluctuations in the response of a subject can be expected to be smaller over shorter periods of time and larger over longer periods—a circumstance which should be evaluated by the experimenter. If the experimenter has each subject appear in a dozen or more conditions requiring several hours of testing, the fluctuations may be so large that any advantage to be gained in using the same subject may be lost. If the experimenter tries to distribute the testing over several days, he may again defeat himself by introducing equally large or larger errors due to fluctuations in the subject's condition over that period of time. For the most effective use of the design, the number of conditions to be imposed on a subject and the total amount of time required of him should be such that relatively small variations in response can be expected.

In conducting an experiment involving c conditions, the experimenter obtains a random sample of r subjects from a specified supply. He schedules an appointment with each subject, at which time the treatments are imposed and the measures on the dependent variable are obtained. The several conditions are assigned randomly to the occasions of measurement. Thus the order of treatment will vary from subject to subject. Since each occasion of measurement will bear an error, the random assignment of conditions to occasions will insure the random distribution of errors over the conditions.

The (rc) observations can be classified into a table of r rows and c columns where columns correspond to conditions and rows correspond to subjects. The analysis of the data and the evaluation are achieved by the same methods used with the matched-group design. The general form of the conventional analysis of variance report is given in Table 9.10. It should be compared with the analyses of Tables 9.6 and 9.9.

Table 9.10
GENERAL ANALYSIS FOR A DESIGN INVOLVING REPEATED TREATMENT AND MEASUREMENT

Component	df	V	F
Treatments	$c - 1$	V_t	V_t/V_e
Subjects	$r - 1$		
Residual error	$(r - 1)(c - 1)$	V_e	
Total	$N - 1$		

c = number of treatments
r = number of subjects
$N = rc$ = total number of observations

When the effects of order are not negligible, the experimenter has two choices. He may continue to randomize the order of imposing conditions on each subject and continue to apply the same analysis. If he does so, the order effects enter the experiment as errors randomized over the several conditions. If these order effects are large, the resulting loss in precision may offset any advantage to be gained by eliminating differences among subjects.

The experimenter's other choice is to apply a *Latin square* in formulating his treatment plan and in classifying his data for analysis. The Latin square is a table of *m* rows and *m* columns, and, consequently, m^2 cells. Each cell contains a single letter. The m^2 letters required to fill the table consist of the first *m* letters of the alphabet, each one occurring *m* times. The letters are assigned so that each different letter appears once, and only once, in each row and column. Table 9.11 gives two examples of Latin squares. Other

Table 9.11
EXAMPLES OF LATIN SQUARES

A	B
B	A

(2 × 2)

A	B	C
C	A	B
B	C	A

(3 × 3)

arrangements of letters are possible in the 2 × 2 and the 3 × 3 squares. Interchanging the different letters will produce new arrangements. Larger squares can, of course, be written.

The Latin letters can be applied to classifying data, just as the rows and columns of a table constitute a basis for classification. Each different Latin letter specifies a category or class. There are *m* such classes in a square table on which a Latin square has been imposed, just as there are m columns and m rows. Furthermore, the variability in a square table of numbers can be analyzed into four additive components: between-column, between-row, between-letter, and residual variability.

To control for order effects in repeated treatment of subjects, the experimenter selects m subjects and assigns one subject to each row of an $m \times m$ table. He then selects, randomly, a Latin square from the totality of squares of that size and assigns m experimental conditions to the subjects according to the positions of Latin letters in the selected square. He then imposes each treatment and measures on the dependent variable following an order given by the order of columns from, say, left to right. The effect of the procedure is to insure that each condition appears once and only once in each ordinal position. In the analysis, the between-row sum of squares contains differences among subjects; the between-column sum of squares contains differences among the m ordinal positions of treatment; the between-letter component is the apparent treatment effect; and the residual variability is a measure of error. The general form of the analysis is given in Table 9.12. In most situations, the design would require replication with several squares.

Table 9.12
GENERAL FORM OF THE ANALYSIS FOR A LATIN SQUARE DESIGN FOR CONTROLLING ORDER EFFECTS

Component	df	V	F
Treatments (letters)	$m - 1$	V_t	V_t/V_e
Order (columns)	$m - 1$		
Subjects (rows)	$m - 1$		
Error (residual)	$m^2 - 3m + 2$	V_e	
Total	$m^2 - 1$		

m = size of the Latin square

In this application of the Latin square, the assumption is made that the effects of a position are constant and additive for all conditions. If this assumption is not met, then order effects will be contained in the error variability. For a more extended consideration of Latin squares, the student should consult articles by Grant[1] and McNemar.[2]

There is little doubt that repeated treatment designs have the advantage over matching designs when measurement can be repeated and when order effects are negligible. An experimental comparison made on a single subject will very likely be affected by a smaller error than one made on a matched pair of subjects. We should also point out that fewer subjects are required for repeated treatment designs than for matching designs to produce the same number of observations. This economy is of considerable importance when subjects are in scant supply.

It is not so clear that repeated treatment designs have the advantage over matching designs when order effects exist. Degrees of freedom are lost from the error term for the position component in Latin square designs. There may be little or no justification for assuming that position effects are additive. The one advantage about which there is no doubt is the smaller number of subjects required.

ANTICIPATION

Matching is not the only way of reducing error by means of pre-experimental measures. In the design to be presented in the next chapter, measures obtained under uniform conditions provide the means of adjusting experimental data. The adjustment is intended to eliminate, as far as possible, differences among subjects.

REFERENCES

1. Grant, D. A., "The Latin Square Principle in the Design and Analysis of Psychological Experiments," *Psychological Bulletin*, 45, 1948, 427–442.
2. McNemar, Q. "On the Use of Latin Squares in Psychology," *Psychological Bulletin*, 48, 1951, 398–401.
3. Pitman, E. J. G., "Significance Tests Which May Be Applied to Samples From Any Populations," *Biometrika*, 29, 1937–38, 322–335.
4. Tukey, J. W., "One Degree of Freedom for Nonadditivity," *Biometrics*, 5, 1949, 232–242.
5. Welch, B. L., "On the Z Test in Randomized Blocks and Latin Squares," *Biometrika*, 29, 1937, 21–52.

ADJUSTING

10

Matching of subjects and repeated treatment of subjects are not the only ways to achieve precision.   There is another design which results in increased precision but does not require that the experimenter actually arrange his materials in a special way, as is the case with the matched group design, to reduce the magnitude of errors in the experimental comparisons.   The increase in precision is accomplished through the medium of a response variable which is known to be correlated with the dependent variable.

The design requires a number of random samples corresponding to the number of conditions.   Measures on the correlated response variable are obtained under uniform conditions prior to the imposition of treatments just as in the matched group design.   No matching or ranking is carried out, however, and the actual reduction of variability, which is called the *adjustment*, is deferred until the final statistical analysis of the data.

The adjustment involves the elimination of a component of error variability in the experimental data.   The variability eliminated consists of differences among subjects, which existed prior to the experiment and which are a potential source of error, since these differences can be estimated from the measures of response obtained before the experiment.   The estimate of the inequalities among subjects is achieved arithmetically by means of either the correlation between the dependent variable and the adjusting variable or the regression of the dependent variable on the adjusting variable.

The design and the method of analysis are often referred to as the *analysis of covariance*.   We shall see that the analysis of covariance can be conceptualized as the analysis of variability in errors of prediction.   It can be shown that the errors of prediction are measures on the dependent variable adjusted for initial differences among subjects through the use of a correlated response variable.

PREDICTION

The account of analysis of covariance will begin with a review of the fundamentals of simple linear regression and correlation, and a consideration of the sources of variability in bivariate distributions.

Given the bivariate distribution of variables X and Y, we may pose the problem of finding a constant, b, which in general permits of the best prediction of y from the corresponding value of x in a linear equation. Note that y and x are deviations from means. The linear equation can be written

$$y' = bx,$$

where x is a deviation from the mean of X, b is the desired constant, and y' is the predicted deviation from the mean of Y.

Since we propose to use the constant, b, in predicting from all values of X, we expect to make errors in the predictions. That is, the predicted deviation, y', for a given value of x, may be different from the actual deviation value, y, which is paired with x. An error in prediction can be written as the difference between a predicted value and an actual value as follows:

$$y - y'.$$

We are now prepared to say in what sense the prediction will be "best." That is, we can now choose a criterion for the selection of a value for the constant, b, which will permit the "best" prediction of y from x. The criterion, which is known as the *least squares* criterion, is that the sum of squares of errors will be a minimum.

The equation states that $y' = bx$. If we substitute bx for y' in $(y - y')$, the error in prediction can then be written as

$$y - bx.$$

The sum of squares of the errors for all N, paired values is

$$\Sigma(y - bx)^2.$$

The methods of calculus provide a solution for the value of the constant which will give a minimum value for the sum of squares. If we differentiate the expression

$$\Sigma(y - bx)^2$$

with respect to b, set the derivative equal to zero, and then solve for b, we find that the value of the constant which satisfies the least squares criterion is the ratio of the sum of products of deviations to the sum of squares of x. The formula is

$$b = \frac{\Sigma xy}{\Sigma x^2}.$$

The variability in Y can now be analyzed with reference to the variability in X. Two components result. One is the sum of squares of the predicted values. The predicted deviations, y', may vary and their variability can be measured by the sum of squares $\Sigma y'^2$, which is said to be the variability in Y associated with, accounted for by, or predicted from the variability in X. The other component is the sum of squares of the errors of prediction,

$$\Sigma(y - y')^2,$$

which is said to be the variability in Y not associated with, not accounted for by, or not predicted from the variability in X.

The variability in Y is equal to the sum of these two components. That is,

$$\Sigma y^2 = \Sigma y'^2 + \Sigma(y - y')^2.$$

It is convenient to express the predicted variability in terms of sums of products and squares. We note that

$$y' = bx.$$

Squaring: $\qquad\qquad\qquad\quad y'^2 = b^2 x^2.$

Summing: $\qquad\qquad\quad \Sigma y'^2 = \Sigma b^2 x^2 = b^2 \Sigma x^2.$

But $b = \Sigma xy / \Sigma x^2$, so, substituting:

$$\Sigma y'^2 = \frac{(\Sigma xy)^2 (\Sigma x^2)}{(\Sigma x^2)^2}.$$

Therefore, $\qquad\qquad\quad \Sigma y'^2 = \frac{(\Sigma xy)^2}{\Sigma x^2}.$

We can now write the sum of squares of errors in prediction as the difference between the variability in Y and the predicted variability. That is,

$$\Sigma y^2 = \Sigma y'^2 + \Sigma(y - y')^2.$$

Transposing:

$$\Sigma(y - y')^2 = \Sigma y^2 - \Sigma y'^2.$$

Substituting for $\Sigma y'^2$ gives

$$\Sigma(y - y')^2 = \Sigma y^2 - \frac{(\Sigma xy)^2}{\Sigma x^2},$$

an equation which expresses the *adjustment* of variability in Y and which, in varied forms, is employed repeatedly in the analysis of covariance.

COMPONENTS OF UNPREDICTED VARIABILITY IN CLASSIFIED NUMBERS

Let us suppose that we have numbers arranged in two groups, I and II. Each group consists of five pairs of numbers. In each pair, one number is classified as X and the other is classified as Y. An example of such a classification of numbers is given in Table 10.1.

Table 10.1

AN EXAMPLE OF PAIRED AND CLASSIFIED NUMBERS

I		II	
X	Y	X	Y
3	7	2	9
2	8	5	10
4	6	3	8
5	9	1	6
1	5	4	7

There are three distinct steps in the analysis we propose to undertake: (a) the adjustment of the total variability in Y, (b) the adjustment of the within-group variability in Y, and (c) computation of the discrepancy between the results of the two adjustments.

First, we adjust the variability in Y, disregarding the classification into two groups. To do so, we express the Y values as deviations from the total mean, then do the same for X. The transformed values are given in Table 10.2. Now we can analyze the variability in Y into two components, the

Table 10.2

THE NUMBERS IN TABLE 10.1 TRANSFORMED TO DEVIATIONS
FROM THE TOTAL MEANS

I		II	
x	y	x	y
0	−0.5	−1	1.5
−1	0.5	2	2.5
1	−1.5	0	0.5
2	1.5	−2	−1.5
−2	−2.5	1	−0.5

predicted variability and errors of prediction. The necessary sums of squares and products are

$$\Sigma y^2 = 22.5,$$
$$\Sigma x^2 = 20,$$
$$\Sigma xy = 12.$$

Note that there are ten terms in each summation and that the deviations are computed with reference to the total mean in each case. The student should be able to verify these summary values by finding the squares and the products of the transformed values in Table 10.2 and summing them.

The predicted variability is given by the ratio

$$\frac{(\Sigma xy)^2}{\Sigma x^2} = \frac{12^2}{20} = 7.2.$$

The unpredicted variability, E_t, is given by the subtraction

$$E_t = \Sigma y^2 - \frac{(\Sigma xy)^2}{\Sigma x^2} = 22.5 - 7.2 = 15.3.$$

Having found E_t to be 15.3, we have completed the first adjustment. Note that E_t is computed from deviations from the total means.

The second step in the analysis is the adjustment of the within-group variability in Y. Refer to Table 10.1 again. We shall express the values of X in group I as deviations from the mean of X for that group, and the values of Y in the same group as deviations from the mean of Y for that group. In a similar fashion, the values in group II are transformed to deviations from the group mean. The results of these operations are given in Table 10.3.

Table 10.3
THE NUMBERS IN TABLE 10.1 TRANSFORMED TO DEVIATIONS FROM THE GROUP MEANS

I		II	
x_k	y_k	x_k	y_k
0	0	−1	1
−1	1	2	2
1	−1	0	0
2	2	−2	−2
−2	−2	1	−1

Now we can analyze the within-group variability in Y into two components: that predicted, P_w, and that not predicted, E_w. The required sums of squares and products are

$$\Sigma y^2 = 20,$$
$$\Sigma x^2 = 20,$$
$$\Sigma xy = 12.$$

These summary values can be obtained from Table 10.3.

The within-group predicted variability is

$$P_w = 12^2/20 = 7.2.$$

The within-group variability not predicted is

$$E_w = 20 - 7.2 = 12.8,$$

and the second adjustment is now completed. Note that E_w is computed from deviations from column means.

Two sums of squares of prediction errors have now been computed. The first of these quantities, E_t, the total sum of squares of errors of prediction, is a measure of the variability in errors of prediction when the classification has been disregarded. The second of these quantities, E_w, the combined within-sample sum of squares of errors of prediction, is a measure of the variability in errors of prediction when only the differences within each group are retained.

The third step in the analysis is the computation of D, a discrepancy sum of squares. The discrepancy sum of squares derives from the following notions. For any value of Y, two errors in prediction can be computed. One of these is the error in prediction when the sums of squares and products are computed with reference to the total means, as in the case of E_t. This error can be represented as

$$y - bx,$$

where x and y are deviations from the total means of X and Y, respectively, and b is the regression coefficient. The other error in prediction occurs when the sums of squares and products are computed with reference to the group means, as in the case of E_w. This second error can be represented as

$$y_k - b_k x_k,$$

where x_k and y_k are deviations from the means of the kth group and b_k is the regression coefficient computed from the combined within-group sums of squares and products.

It is possible that the two errors of prediction associated with each value of Y will differ. A discrepancy, d, between the two errors is given by

$$d = (y - bx) - (y_k - b_k x_k).$$

These discrepancies may vary, and their variability can be measured. Since the mean of the discrepancies is always zero, the sum of squared deviations is the sum of the squares of the discrepancies themselves. If we call this sum of squares D, then

$$D = \Sigma d^2.$$

A single error, $(y - bx)$, can now be conceived of as consisting of two additive parts. One part is the error in predicting from the within-group variability, $(y_k - b_k x_k)$. The second part is a discrepancy, d. The relation can be written as

$$(y - bx) = (y_k - b_k x_k) + d.$$

A similar relation obtains for the three corresponding sums of squares. That is,

$$E_t = E_w + D.$$

It is convenient to compute the discrepancy sum of squares, D, by

$$D = E_t - E_w.$$

In the numerical example given above, $E_t = 15.3$ and $E_w = 12.8$. Then

$$D = 15.3 - 12.8 = 2.5.$$

With the two adjustments and computation of the discrepancy between the two results, the analysis of variability in errors of prediction for classified numbers has been completed.

THEORY

We assume a normal bivariate population of observations which defines a population of errors of prediction. The errors of prediction are normally distributed around the regression line with a uniform variance. We obtain c samples of paired observations.

Observations in the c samples can be combined without regard for the sample in which they occur and E_t, the total sum of squares of errors of prediction, can be computed. E_t can then be analyzed into two components.

The first component is E_w, the sum of squares of errors of prediction computed from the within-sample variability and covariation. The second component is D, the sum of squares of the discrepancies in the two sets of errors of prediction.

Two unbiased estimates of the variance of the population of errors of estimate can be computed. The first estimate, V_{ew}, is computed by dividing E_w by $(N - c - 1)$ degrees of freedom, where N is the total number of observations and c is the number of samples. That is,

$$V_{ew} = \frac{E_w}{(N - c - 1)}.$$

The second unbiased estimate, V_d, which is obtained by dividing D, the sum of squares of discrepancies in the two sets of errors of estimate, by $(c - 1)$ degrees of freedom. That is,

$$V_d = \frac{D}{(c - 1)}.$$

The ratio of the discrepancy variance, V_d, to the variance of the within-sample errors of prediction, V_{ew}, is the comparison of interest to us. The ratio is distributed as the F function for $(c - 1)$ and $(N - c - 1)$ degrees of freedom. That is,

$$F = \frac{V_d}{V_{ew}}.$$

PRACTICE

A uniformity trial would consist of the following operations.

The investigator enumerates a supply of subjects. He then obtains the desired number of random samples from the supply.

He selects a response variable as the dependent variable for the trial and another response variable for use in adjusting measures on the dependent variable. He knows that the dependent variable is linearly correlated, or approximately so, with the adjusting variable.

He measures all subjects under uniform conditions on the adjusting variable and again under uniform conditions on the dependent variable. In both instances, he assigns each subject to an occasion of measurement by random methods.

The uniformity trial is now complete and the data for the trial are available for analysis. The theoretical analysis of errors of prediction described above can be applied to the uniformity trial data.

The predicted variability reflects the magnitude of differences among subjects as these differences are revealed in the consistency of the measures from the first occasion to the second. The greater the differences among subjects, the higher the correlation between adjusting variable and dependent variable. The higher the correlation, the greater the proportion of variability predicted.

The variability not predicted consists of inconsistencies in response from one occasion to another.

The predicted variability and the errors of prediction are both subject to the effects of randomization. Furthermore, the discrepancy sum of squares, $D = E_t - E_w$, is also subject to the effects of random error.

THE FORMAL EXPERIMENT

We shall now consider the sources of variability in errors of prediction in experimental data, where the observed variability is due to sampling errors and the possible effects of treatments. Again we would like to identify two components. One component, which is to be evaluated, will contain, in unknown proportions, variability due to treatment and variability due to random errors. The other component, which will serve as a standard for the evaluation, will contain only sampling error.

In conducting an experiment with a single independent variable, the investigator obtains two or more random samples of subjects. He measures the subjects in all samples on an adjusting variable under uniform conditions. He next assigns randomly one treatment to each sample, imposes the treatments, and obtains measures of response on the dependent variable. Table 10.4 shows how the data can be tabulated for two conditions, A and B.

Table 10.4
ARRANGEMENT OF CONDITIONS, SUBJECTS AND MEASURES FOR A SIMPLE COVARIANCE DESIGN

Conditions

	A				B	
	Sample 1				Sample 2	
	1	X_{11}	Y_{11}		1	X_{12}	Y_{12}
	2	X_{21}	Y_{21}		2	X_{22}	Y_{22}
	3	X_{31}	Y_{31}		3	X_{32}	Y_{32}
Subjects	·	·	·	Subjects	·	·	·
	i	X_{i1}	Y_{i1}		i	X_{i2}	Y_{i2}
	·	·	·		·	·	·
	n	X_{n1}	Y_{n1}		n	X_{n2}	Y_{n2}

X_{ik} = Pre-experimental measure on ith subject in kth sample
Y_{ik} = Observation on ith subject in kth sample after treatment

The total variability in Y over the entire table contains the possible effects of treatment and errors. As we have said before, in psychological research the random errors consist, in part, of differences among subjects. Differences on the adjusting variable, X, do not contain the effects of treatment, since they occurred with uniform conditions for all subjects. To the extent that differences among subjects on the adjusting variable are correlated with differences on the dependent variable, error in the dependent variable can be eliminated. In terms of correlation theory, the part which can be eliminated will be the variability in the dependent variable associated with, accounted for by, or predicted from variability in the adjusting variable. In a logical sense, the part eliminated will consist of differences among subjects which existed prior to the experiment, as suggested by the differences observed on the adjusting variable, and which appear again in the experimental data.

Consider the first adjustment that is performed in the analysis. It can be written as follows:

$$\begin{matrix} \text{Total} \\ \text{variability} \end{matrix} - \begin{matrix} \text{Predicted} \\ \text{variability} \end{matrix} = \begin{matrix} \text{Variability of} \\ \text{errors of prediction.} \end{matrix}$$

Treatment effects are contained in the total variability. What happens to them in the adjustment? When treatment effects are constant and additive, they will be uncorrelated with the adjusting variable and, consequently, will not be contained in the predicted variability. Treatment effects will be left in the errors of prediction, the remainder in the adjustment. To be more exact, we should say that the differential effects of the treatments will be uncorrelated with the adjusting variable in the long run, or on the average over an indefinitely large number of experiments. The correlation between treatment effects and the adjusting variable in any single experiment will be due, in part, to chance. The guarantee that treatment effects and the adjusting variable will be uncorrelated in the long run is contained in the actual random assignment of treatments to subjects. Since the conjunction of a given treatment and a given subject is a random event, the differences among treatments should not be related to the differences among subjects on the adjusting variable.

After the first adjustment, treatment effects will be contained in E_t, the total errors of prediction. E_t will contain error, of course, in addition to treatment effects. Differences among subjects in the experiment, to the extent that they can be predicted from measures obtained prior to the experiment, are eliminated in the adjustment and are not contained in E_t.

Consider now the second adjustment. It can be written:

$$\text{Within-group variability} - \text{Within-group predicted variability} = \text{Within-group errors of prediction.}$$

Constant and additive treatment effects are not contained in any of these components. Keep in mind that the adjusting variable can not be affected by treatments. Recall, too, that constant, additive effects do not change the within-group variability of the dependent variable. The within-group variability contains only sampling error. The within-group predicted variability is a measure of differences among subjects treated alike in the experiment, as these differences can be predicted from pre-experimental measures. The within-group errors of prediction are sampling errors that cannot be predicted and therefore cannot be removed.

Thus the second adjustment yields E_w, the sum of squares of the within-group errors of prediction, a measure of the sampling error actually affecting the experiment.

The computation of the discrepancy sum of squares is the third step in the analysis. The difference between E_t and E_w will be the treatment effect, except for the bias due to the random errors which have not been eliminated. The subtraction can be written as

$$\text{Variability of errors of prediction} - \text{Within-group errors of prediction} = \text{Discrepancy variability}$$

It is not so simple that we can say, "Subtracting error from a component that contains treatment effects and error yields treatment effects." The error we subtract is actually only an estimate of the error in the other component, so that the discrepancy sum of squares is a measure of treatment effect with a bias attached. The discrepancy component is the apparent treatment effect and must be evaluated.

The treatment variance is computed by dividing the discrepancy sum of squares by $(c - 1)$ degrees of freedom. The error variance is computed by dividing the within-group sum of squares of errors of prediction by $(N - c - 1)$ degrees of freedom. For the test of significance, the treatment variance is compared to the error variance in an F ratio and the null hypothesis is accepted or rejected.

It will be instructive to examine the first of the two adjustments with respect to the effect of that adjustment on the group or treatment means. From such an examination we shall see that the means of groups on the dependent variable are appropriately adjusted for initial differences among the groups, and that the adjustment of the means corresponds to the reduction of the estimate of the error to which the means are liable. The importance of this correspondence can be seen by considering the effect of reducing the estimate of error without adjusting the differences among means and the effect of adjusting the differences among means without reducing the estimate of error. Reduction of the estimate of error without corresponding adjustment of the differences among means would lead to the announcement of too many significant results, that is, an increase in the probability of an error of the first kind. Adjusting the differences among means without a corresponding reduction of the estimate of error would lead to the announcement of too few significant results, that is, an increase in the probability of an error of the second kind.

The total variability in the data is measured with reference to the total mean, $\bar{Y}_{..}$. If we eliminate from consideration all the variability except that which is to be evaluated, we are, in effect, concerned with the variability of a set of adjusted observations whose deviations from the total mean are the discrepancies, d, between corresponding values in the two sets of errors of prediction. A discrepancy between two errors of estimate has been represented as

$$d = (y - bx) - (y_k - b_k x_k).$$

An adjusted observation can be written as

$$\bar{Y}_{..} + d$$

or as

$$\bar{Y}_{..} + (y - bx) - (y_k - b_k x_k).$$

To find the mean of these adjusted observations for a single sample, we must sum the values and divide by n. Summing for a single sample yields

$$n\bar{Y}_{..} + \Sigma y - b\Sigma x.$$

Substituting $(Y - \bar{Y}_{..})$ for y and $(X - \bar{X}_{..})$ for x gives us

$$n\bar{Y}_{..} + \Sigma Y - n\bar{Y}_{..} - b\Sigma X + bn\bar{X}_{..}$$

Combining terms and dividing by n yields the adjusted mean

$$\bar{Y}_k - b\bar{X}_k + b\bar{X}_{..},$$

which can be written as

$$\bar{Y}_k - b(\bar{X}_k - \bar{X}..),$$

in which we see that the sample means on the dependent variable are adjusted for initial differences among the samples. That is to say, each sample mean for the dependent variable is adjusted by an amount predicted from the initial deviation of the sample mean from the total mean on the adjusting variable.

A corresponding reduction in the estimate of error is achieved in the adjustment of the within-group variability to provide the within-group errors of prediction.

SIGNIFICANCE OF REGRESSION

The use of the adjusting variable to eliminate error from experimental data presupposes the existence of a relation between the adjusting variable and the dependent variable. If the two variables are uncorrelated, there will be no advantage in using the method of analysis. As a matter of fact, there will be a slight disadvantage when the two variables are uncorrelated because one degree of freedom is lost from the estimate of error as a consequence of the adjustment.

As a matter of routine practice, the experimenter should examine the relation between the two variables, as it appears in his data, before proceeding with the analysis. If he concludes from the examination that the two variables are correlated, he should proceed with the adjustments as described above. If he concludes they are not correlated, he should abandon the adjusting variable and proceed with the usual analysis of variance for independent samples, in which case his attempt to increase the precision of the design will have failed.

The examination and evaluation of the relation between the adjusting variable and the dependent variable is made possible by a test of significance of the regression. Certain quantities which appeared in the second adjustment of the main analysis are required for the regression test. One of these quantities is the within-sample predicted sum of squares, P_w. The other is E_w, the within-sample sum of squares of errors of prediction. A predicted variance, V_{pw}, is computed by dividing P_w by one degree of freedom. An error variance, V_{ew}, is computed, as before, by dividing E_w by $(N - c - 1)$ degree of freedom. The variance ratio for the test of significance of regression is

$$F = \frac{V_{pw}}{V_{ew}}.$$

HOMOGENEITY OF ERROR VARIANCES

Nonadditive treatment effects may produce heterogeneous sample variances and may, as a consequence, produce heterogeneity in the components of the estimate of error. A biased estimate of error will result. A test of the homogeneity of the sample variances has been described in connection with the design employing random samples with no matching or adjusting (see page 54). The same test can be applied here.

When the departures from additivity for a given condition are correlated with the adjusting variable, the correlation between adjusting variable and dependent variable for that sample will be changed. The result may be heterogeneous sample regressions and again heterogeneous components of the error variance. Since the estimate of error will be biased when the components in the estimate are heterogenous, the observed regressions should be examined and a test of significance of their homogeneity should be performed.

The test of homogeneity of regressions requires the computation of errors of prediction for each sample separately. These are combined into a quantity we shall designate as E_i, the combined sums of squares of errors of prediction for the individual samples. In other words, the adjustment

$$\Sigma y^2 - \frac{(\Sigma xy)^2}{\Sigma x^2}$$

is applied to each sample separately, resulting in a sum of squares of errors of prediction for each sample. These sums of squares of errors of prediction for the individual samples are then added, yielding E_i.

A measure of the heterogeneity of the several sample regressions is given by subtracting E_i from E_w, the within-sample sum of squares of errors of prediction computed by combining sums of squares and products before the adjustment is effected. Note that E_w occurs in the main analysis and again in the test of significance of the regression.

The test of significance is again an F ratio. The variance for the numerator is computed by dividing the difference

$$E_w - E_i$$

by $(c - 1)$ degrees of freedom. The variance for the denominator of F is computed by dividing E_i by $(N - 2c)$ degrees of freedom.

In a properly conducted experiment, measures on the adjusting variable, having been obtained under uniform conditions, will contain only sampling errors. Consequently there is no reason to test the sample variances on the adjusting variable for heterogeneity. If an investigator, having examined the sample variances on the adjusting variable and having discovered unusual differences among them, should then discard the materials and select others, he would be changing the probabilities associated with the results of his experimental comparisons in some indeterminate fashion.

AN EXAMPLE WITH FORMULAS

The analysis of covariance will now be applied to data from the experiment on cheating first described in Chapter 2. The student may recall that an analysis of variance of these data, presented in Chapter 6, did not yield significant results. The cheating scores are tabulated in Table 10.5 for the

Table 10.5
PAIRED MEASURES FOR THE CHEATING EXPERIMENT

Control group		Reward group	
X	Y	X	Y
13	4	5	4
11	6	9	1
17	11	23	15
22	13	12	3
7	5	9	0
9	2	17	5
12	7	15	8
7	0	4	2
4	2	0	0
5	0	8	-1
1	0	2	0
12	11	7	1
2	0	4	0
3	0	1	0
1	1	4	0
5	1	6	0
7	6	3	0
18	10	10	-1
2	0		

X is the actual error score
Y is the cheating score

two groups of children. Paired with each cheating score is the actual error score made by the child on the test. The actual error score was determined by the experimenter without the child's knowledge.

The experimenter reasoned that initial differences, which would predict the cheating they would engage in later, may have existed among the children. She further reasoned that some portion of the final differences in cheating might be related to initial differences as measured by the actual test performance.   The possibility that high error scores would tend to go with high cheating scores and low error scores with low cheating scores is simply explained.   The child who made a few errors had little incentive to cheat and, as a matter of fact, little opportunity.   The child who made many errors may have had greater incentive and certainly had greater opportunity. Actual test performance (the error score determined by the experimenter) was chosen, therefore, as an adjusting variable, and differences in cheating scores were adjusted for differences in actual test performance.

Computation of the total sum of squares and the within-sample sum of squares for the dependent variable, Y, is given in Chapter 6.   The total sum of squares was found to be

$$666.32.$$

The combined within-sample sum of squares is

$$625.47.$$

Computation of the total and the within-sample sums of squares for the adjusting variable, X, will be undertaken next.

The formula for the total sum of squares of X, adapted from formula (4.2), is

$$\Sigma X^2 - C'_x.$$

Summary data:

$$\Sigma X = 297,$$

$$(\Sigma X)^2 = 88,209,$$

$$N = 37,$$

$$C'_x = \frac{(\Sigma X)^2}{N} = 2384.03,$$

$$\Sigma X^2 = 3673.$$

Computation: $3673 - 2384.03 = 1288.97$.

The formula for the within-sample sum of squares for X, for any sample, adapted from formula (4.1):

$$\Sigma X^2 - \frac{(\Sigma X)^2}{n}.$$

Summary data for the control group:

$$\Sigma X = 158,$$
$$(\Sigma X)^2 = 24{,}964,$$
$$n = 19,$$
$$\Sigma X^2 = 1988.$$

Computation: $1988 - 24{,}964/19 = 674.11.$

Summary data for the reward group:

$$\Sigma X = 139,$$
$$(\Sigma X)^2 = 19{,}321,$$
$$n = 18,$$
$$\Sigma X^2 = 1685.$$

Computation: $1685 - 19{,}321/18 = 611.61.$

Next we combine the within-sample sums of squares of X for the two groups: $674.11 + 611.61 = 1285.72.$

The formula for the total sum of products of deviations, Σxy, is

$$\Sigma xy = \Sigma XY - \frac{(\Sigma X)(\Sigma Y)}{N}. \tag{10.1}$$

Formula (10.1) can be derived from the expression

$$\Sigma(X - \bar{X}_{..})(Y - \bar{Y}_{..})$$

by applying the simplification rules and making appropriate substitutions.

Summary data:

$$\Sigma X = 297,$$
$$\Sigma Y = 116,$$
$$\Sigma XY = 1708,$$
$$N = 37.$$

Computation: $1708 - (297)(116)/37 = 776.86$

The formula for the within-sample sum of products for any sample, adapted from formula (10.1), is

$$\Sigma xy = \Sigma XY - \frac{(\Sigma X)(\Sigma Y)}{n}$$

Summary data for the control group:

$$\Sigma X = 158,$$
$$\Sigma Y = 79,$$
$$\Sigma XY = 1096,$$
$$n = 19.$$

Computation: $1096 - (158)(79)/19 = 439.05$.
Summary data for the reward group:

$$\Sigma X = 139,$$
$$\Sigma Y = 37,$$
$$\Sigma XY = 612,$$
$$n = 18.$$

Computation: $612 - (139)(37)/18 = 326.28$.
Combining the within-sample sums of products for the two groups gives:

$$439.05 + 326.28 = 765.33.$$

The first adjustment, based on the sums of squares and products of deviations from the total means:

$$E_t = \Sigma y^2 - \frac{(\Sigma xy)^2}{\Sigma x^2}$$

$$= 666.32 - \frac{(776.86)^2}{1288.97} = 198.11$$

The second adjustment, based on the within-sample sums of squares and products of deviations from the sample means:

$$E_w = \Sigma \Sigma y^2 - \frac{(\Sigma \Sigma xy)^2}{\Sigma \Sigma x^2}$$

$$= 625.47 - \frac{(765.33)^2}{1285.72} = 169.90.$$

Computation of D, the discrepancy sum of squares, is next:

$$D = E_t - E_w$$
$$= 198.11 - 169.90 = 28.21.$$

Computation of V_d, the discrepancy variance, a measure of the apparent treatment effect:

$$V_d = \frac{D}{(c-1)}$$

$$= \frac{28.21}{1} = 28.21.$$

Computation of V_{ew}, the error variance:

$$V_{ew} = \frac{E_w}{(N-c-1)}$$

$$= \frac{169.90}{34} = 5.00.$$

Computation of F for the test of significance:

$$F = \frac{V_d}{V_{ew}}$$

$$F = \frac{28.21}{5.00} = 5.64.$$

The criterion value of F for 1 and 34 degrees of freedom is 4.13. The obtained value of F exceeds the criterion, and the null hypothesis is rejected. The experimenter concluded that the differing instructions had different effects on the behavior of the children.

Table 10.6 contains a summary of the results.

Table 10.6
ANALYSIS OF COVARIANCE OF DATA IN TABLE 10.5

Component of variability		SS	df	V	F	F_c
Treatment	(D)	28.21	1	28.21	5.64*	4.13
Error	(E_w)	169.90	34	5.00		
Total	(E_t)	198.11	35			

* $F > F_c$; Null hypothesis rejected

It is common practice to report values for the adjusted means so that the direction of the significant difference can be determined. A formula for the adjustment of a sample mean was derived on page 120. The formula was

$$\bar{Y}_k - b(\bar{X}_k - \bar{X}_{..}).$$

Computation of b, the regression coefficient, and $\bar{X}..$, the total mean of the adjusting variable:

$$b = \frac{\Sigma xy}{\Sigma x^2}$$

$$= \frac{776.86}{1288.97} = 0.6027,$$

$$\bar{X}.. = \frac{\Sigma X}{N}$$

$$= \frac{297}{37} = 8.03.$$

Computation of the means, $\bar{Y}_k$ and $\bar{X}_k$, for the control group:

$$\bar{Y}_k = \frac{\Sigma Y}{n} = \frac{79}{19} = 4.16$$

$$\bar{X}_k = \frac{\Sigma X}{n} = \frac{158}{19} = 8.32.$$

The adjustment of the control group mean:

$$\bar{Y}_k - b(\bar{X}_k - \bar{X}..),$$

$$4.16 - 0.6027(8.32 - 8.03) = 3.99.$$

Computation of the means, $\bar{Y}_k$ and $\bar{X}_k$, for the reward group:

$$\bar{Y}_k = \frac{\Sigma Y}{n} = \frac{37}{18} = 2.06,$$

$$\bar{X}_k = \frac{\Sigma X}{n} = \frac{139}{18} = 7.72.$$

The adjustment of the reward group mean:

$$\bar{Y}_k - b(\bar{X}_k - \bar{X}..),$$

$$2.06 - 0.6027(7.72 - 8.03) = 2.25.$$

Inspection of the two adjusted means reveals that the reward group had lower cheating scores than did the control group. The analysis of variance described in Chapter 6 led to the acceptance of the null hypothesis and the conclusion that observed differences between the two groups were due to random errors. When the two groups of observations are adjusted for initial differences in performance, the analysis results in rejection of the null hypothesis. Of course, from these results we cannot say what would happen if we repeated this experiment many times. We do know that, if the correlation between adjusting variable and dependent variable is real and substantial, the precision of the design is increased by the use of the covariance analysis and the power of the test of significance is increased.

SIGNIFICANCE OF REGRESSION

It is usually a matter of routine practice to test the significance of the regression of the dependent variable on the adjusting variable before proceeding with the main analysis. This order of events has not been followed here because it seemed easier to describe the computing procedures by beginning with the main analysis summarized in Table 10.6. Computing procedures for the test of significance of the regression will be given next.

In the second adjustment of the main analysis, the predicted sum of squares, P_w, based on the within-sample sums of squares and products was

$$P_w = \frac{(\Sigma \Sigma xy)^2}{\Sigma \Sigma x^2} = \frac{(765.33)^2}{1285.72} = 455.57.$$

The predicted variance, V_{pw}, is computed as follows:

$$V_{pw} = \frac{P_w}{1} = \frac{455.57}{1} = 455.57.$$

Also computed for the second adjustment was the within-sample sum of squares of errors of estimate, E_w, which was found to be 169.90. The corresponding variance, V_{ew}, was 5.00.

The test of significance of regression involves the variance ratio,

$$F = \frac{V_{pw}}{V_{ew}} = \frac{455.57}{5.00} = 91.11.$$

The criterion value of F for 1 and 34 degrees of freedom is 4.13. The obtained value exceeds the criterion, and the null hypothesis is rejected. We conclude that the assumption of a real correlation between the two variables is justified and that use of actual test performance as an adjusting variable would be worthwhile in partially eliminating error from the data.

It is worth noting that the ratio of the predicted variability, P_w, to the within-sample variability is the proportion of error variability eliminated. The proportion is $455.57/625.47 = 0.73$. The within-sample linear correlation between X and Y is $\sqrt{0.73} = 0.85$.

HOMOGENEITY OF COMPONENTS OF ERROR

The two sample variances were tested in Chapter 6. The ratio in the test of homogeneity was

$$F = 19.70/15.94 = 1.24.$$

It is not significant, and the assumption of homogeneity is justified.

The test of homogeneity of the two sample regressions will be described next. The formula for the adjustment of the dependent variable on a single sample is

$$\Sigma y^2 - \frac{(\Sigma xy)^2}{\Sigma x^2}.$$

Substituting values already obtained for the control group gives

$$354.53 - (439.05)^2/674.11 = 68.58.$$

Substituting values obtained for the reward group gives

$$270.94 - (326.28)^2/611.61 = 96.88.$$

Combining these two sums of squares of errors of prediction yields the quantity we have designated E_i. That is,

$$E_i = 68.58 + 96.88 = 165.46.$$

E_w, the sum of squares of errors of prediction obtained by combining the within-sample sums of squares and products before adjusting, has been determined to be 169.90.

A measure of the heterogeneity of the regressions is given by

$$(E_w - E_i) = 169.90 - 165.46 = 4.44.$$

Dividing $(E_w - E_i)$ by $(c - 1)$ yields the variance for the numerator of the F ratio for the test of homogeneity of regressions:

$$4.44/1 = 4.44.$$

Dividing E_i by $(N - 2c)$ gives the variance for the denominator:

$$165.46/33 = 5.01.$$

Then

$$F = 4.44/5.01 = 0.89$$

The obtained F is not significant, and the assumption that the two sample regressions are homogeneous is taken to be justified.

The individual regression lines and the combined regression line for the two samples have been plotted in Fig. 10.1. The formula for a sample regression coefficient, the slope of the regression line, is

$$b = \frac{\Sigma xy}{\Sigma x^2}.$$

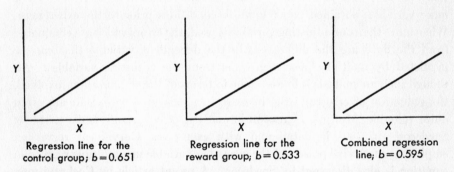

Regression line for the control group; $b = 0.651$ Regression line for the reward group; $b = 0.533$ Combined regression line; $b = 0.595$

Fig. 10.1   Plots of the individual regression lines and the combined regression line for the two samples in the experiment on cheating.

For the control group, $b = 439.05/674.11 = 0.651$.   For the reward group, $b = 326.28/611.61 = 0.533$.

The formula for b_k, the coefficient for the combined regression, is

$$b_k = \frac{\Sigma \Sigma xy}{\Sigma \Sigma x^2}.$$

Substituting the combined within-sample products and squares gives $b_k = 765.33/1285.72 = 0.595$.

The heterogeneity of the sample regressions is evaluated in terms of their deviations from the combined regression line, which might be thought of as a kind of average.   A measure of the deviations of the individual sample lines from the combined line is obtained by comparing errors of prediction for the combined line with the combined errors of prediction for the individual sample lines. That is, the difference, $(E_w - E_i)$, is a measure of the heterogeneity of the regressions.

ERRORS OF THE SECOND KIND IN ANALYSIS OF COVARIANCE

In a covariance design, the probability of errors of the second kind is a function of the size of the samples, the heterogeneity of the supply, the magnitude of the actual effect of the treatments, and the correlation between the adjusting variable and the dependent variable. The higher the correlation, the more successful will be the attempted reduction of errors and the lower will be the probability of errors of the second kind. In the covariance design described above, only one adjusting variable was employed. The analysis of covariance is not limited to one adjusting variable. It is sometimes possible to adjust simultaneously for differences in measures on two or more variables obtained under uniform conditions prior to the experiment. When more than one adjusting variable is used, the errors which are eliminated from the data are the differences in the dependent variable that can be predicted by multiple linear regression from the adjusting variables. Although such an analysis is burdensome in terms of the computation involved, the reduction of error and the increase in precision which result are often quite valuable. Multiple regression in analysis of covariance is discussed by Snedecor[2] (p. 340) in detail and with examples. Curvilinear regression employing successive powers of the adjusting variable in a multiple regression equation is also discussed by Snedecor. A recent article by Cochran[1] may be of interest for additional reading.

DIFFERENCE MEASURES

Given a dependent variable, Y, and a linearly correlated variable, X, on which pre-experimental measures under uniform conditions have been obtained, the psychologist can effect a simple transformation which will reduce the inequalities among subjects. The transformation

$$Y_{ik} - X_{ik}$$

is justified by the following reasoning:

Let Y_{i1} be a measure on any subject under a given condition and Y_{i2} be a measure on any subject under another condition. The comparison

$$Y_{i1} - Y_{i2}$$

will be biased by whatever difference there was between the two subjects prior to the experiment.

Let X_{i1} and X_{i2} be pre-experimental measures on these same subjects under uniform conditions. The difference between the two subjects that biases the experimental comparison is

$$X_{i1} - X_{i2}.$$

The apparent treatment difference can be corrected for the initial difference between the two subjects by

$$(Y_{i1} - Y_{i2}) - (X_{i1} - X_{i2}).$$

A regrouping of terms in the corrected comparison yields

$$(Y_{i1} - X_{i1}) - (Y_{i2} - X_{i2}),$$

which indicates that the experimental comparison can be corrected by computing a difference for each subject,

$$Y_{ik} - X_{ik},$$

and then comparing these differences.

Since the initial differences among subjects are not the only source of errors, the corrected comparisons are suspect. Errors of measurement, uncontrolled influences, and failures in the correcting may have biased them. The corrected comparisons must be evaluated in relation to an estimate of the error which has not been eliminated. It is quite possible, however, that the error in the corrected comparisons is much smaller than the error in the uncorrected ones.

In conducting an experiment in which he will use difference measures, the psychologist obtains two or more random samples from a supply. He then measures all subjects under uniform conditions on the response variable, X. He next imposes the conditions of the experiment and obtains measures on the dependent variable, Y.

If two conditions, A and B, are imposed on two samples of n subjects, the data can be tabulated as shown in Table 10.7. A difference, $(Y_{ik} - X_{ik})$,

Table 10.7
ARRANGEMENT OF CONDITIONS, SUBJECTS, AND DATA YIELDING DIFFERENCE MEASURES

Conditions

	A				B	
	Sample 1				Sample 2	
	1	X_{11}	Y_{11}		1	X_{12}	Y_{12}
	2	X_{21}	Y_{21}		2	X_{22}	Y_{22}
	3	X_{31}	Y_{31}		3	X_{32}	Y_{32}
Subjects	$\cdot$	$\cdot$	$\cdot$	Subjects	$\cdot$	$\cdot$	$\cdot$
	i	X_{i1}	Y_{i1}		i	X_{i2}	Y_{i2}
	$\cdot$	$\cdot$	$\cdot$		$\cdot$	$\cdot$	$\cdot$
	n	X_{n1}	Y_{n1}		n	X_{n2}	Y_{n2}

X_{ik} = Pre-experimental measure on ith subject in kth sample
Y_{ik} = Observation on ith subject in kth sample after treatment

is computed for each subject. Table 10.8 displays the differences, D_{ik}, upon which the analysis is performed.

Table 10.8
ARRANGEMENT OF DIFFERENCE MEASURES

Conditions

A	B
Sample 1	Sample 2
D_{11}	D_{12}
D_{21}	D_{22}
D_{31}	D_{32}
$\cdot$	$\cdot$
D_{i1}	D_{i2}
$\cdot$	$\cdot$
D_{n1}	D_{n2}

$D_{ik} = (Y_{ik} - X_{ik}) = a$ difference measure on the ith subject in the kth sample

The total variability in the differences is analyzed into two components: the between-sample variability which is the apparent treatment effect and the within-sample variability which provides an estimate of error. The computing procedures for sums of squares, variances, and F are identical with those given for the analysis of variance in Chapter 6. The general form of the table of results is given in Table 10.9.

Table 10.9
GENERAL ANALYSIS OF VARIANCE OF DIFFERENCES

Component of variability	df	V	F
Treatments	$(c - 1)$	V_t	V_t/V_e
Error	$(N - c)$	V_e	
Total	$(N - 1)$		

c = number of conditions or treatments
N = total number of subjects

ERRORS OF THE SECOND KIND FOR DIFFERENCES

Employing difference measures will increase the precision of an experiment under certain, but not all, circumstances. When the variances of X and Y are equal and the true correlation between X and Y is greater than 0.50, there will be a gain in precision. With equal variances and the true correlation less than 0.50, there will be a loss in precision.

We can show that the variance of the difference, $(Y - X)$, is in part a function of the parametric correlation between the two variables. When the variances of X and Y are equal and the parametric correlation is less than 0.50, the variability of the differences will actually be greater than the variability of Y, and, as a result, the chances of detecting a treatment difference of a given magnitude will be poorer when differences are employed. On the other hand, when the parametric correlation is greater than 0.50, the variability of the difference measures will be less than that of the final measures, the means of differences will vary less than means of Y, and the chances of detecting a treatment difference will be better than when no adjustment at all is made.

With unequal variances, the situation is somewhat more complex. It can be shown that when $(\sigma_x/2\sigma_y)$ is less than the true correlation, precision will be gained. However, when $(\sigma_x/2\sigma_y)$ is greater than the true correlation, precision will be lost. (This issue is discussed more fully and with references in Chapter 17.)

The two variables, X and Y, have been discussed as if they were always different response variables. This is not always the case. They may, on occasion, be two measures of the same response, obtained at different times.

Since large differences among subjects are characteristic of many psychological response variables, the true correlation, when X and Y are actually the same variable, is often greater than 0.50. In this case, the variances of X and Y can be expected to be approximately equal. The design, therefore, offers good possibilities for reducing the probability of errors of the second kind.

A PROBLEM

An instructor in physical education wanted to examine the relation between success at attempts from the free-throw line in basketball and exposure to a five-minute, informal lecture on the importance of relaxation.

Two samples of ten subjects each were drawn from 220 male, physical education majors. Each of the 20 subjects was given 100 free throws as a test of his skill prior to the experiment. The number of successful attempts was recorded for each subject. The subjects in the experimental group were then given the talk on the advantages of relaxing. The control subjects were allowed to rest for five minutes. Finally, each subject was allowed 100 free throws and again the number of his successes was recorded.

The data are given in Table 10.10. Evaluate the results. Does analysis of covariance give the same results as the analysis of difference measures?

Table 10.10
SCORES FROM THE BASKETBALL FREE THROW EXPERIMENT

Conditions			
Control		Experimental	
Initial	Final	Initial	Final
38	34	32	35
35	33	35	37
56	56	43	44
42	42	30	30
56	55	43	42
47	48	38	40
61	60	41	44
50	51	63	65
64	66	47	51
69	72	50	56

REFERENCES

1. Cochran, W.G., "Analysis of Covariance: Its Nature and Uses," *Biometrics*, 13, 1957, 261–281.
2. Snedecor, G.W., *Statistical Methods*. Ames, Iowa: The Iowa State College Press, 1946.

FACTORIAL DESIGNS

11

Factorial designs are those designs in which two or more independent variables are manipulated simultaneously and independently of one another. Each independent variable is a set of two or more conditions, and varied combinations of these conditions are imposed on subjects by the experimenter. Observations are then made to determine the effect of the manipulation on a response variable. There is a method of analysis by which it is possible to attribute effects to each of the independent variables and to their interaction.

We shall first examine certain typical treatment plans, or ways of combining conditions, and the comparisons that the plans make possible. These comparisons are implicit in the computation of components of variability in experimental data, but are often obscured by the complexity of the computations. There is a certain logic underlying the comparisons, and the experimenter should be aware of it. If he does not understand the nature of the comparisons, he will not understand what kinds of questions can be answered by the analyses applied to factorial designs.

TREATMENT PLANS

Imagine that we have two independent variables, A and B. Each variable is represented by two conditions or levels. A is represented by conditions A_1 and A_2, where A_1 is either the absence of treatment or a lower level and A_2 is either the presence of treatment or a higher level. Variable B is also represented in the treatment plan by two conditions, B_1 and B_2, the absence and presence or lower and higher levels of treatment.

The two levels of A and the two levels of B can be combined to provide a two-factor treatment plan as shown in Plan 11.1. The levels of each variable are placed on one of the margins of the 2×2 table. In each cell is a symbol

137

representing a combination of conditions. The presence of A and B in the combination is indicated ab. The presence of A and the absence of B is

	A_1	A_2
B_1	1	a
B_2	b	ab

Plan 11.1 Two-factor treatment plan with two levels of each factor.

indicated by a; the absence of A and the presence of B, by b; and the absence of both, by 1. (Combinations of lower and higher levels could be indicated in the same way.)

Four simple comparisons can be obtained with these treatment combinations. They are described below in symbols and words:

$$a - 1 = \text{the effect of } A \text{ in the absence of } B;$$
$$ab - b = \text{the effect of } A \text{ in the presence of } B;$$
$$b - 1 = \text{the effect of } B \text{ in the absence of } A;$$
$$ab - a = \text{the effect of } B \text{ in the presence of } A.$$

Note that, in each comparison, the two combinations differ in only one respect. Thus, a comparison yielding the effect of A involves combinations which differ only with respect to the presence and absence of A.

Two of the four comparisons, $(a - 1)$ and $(ab - b)$, give the effect of A. Since the two effects may not be the same, it will be of interest to us to define a *general* or *main* effect of A by combining the two specific effects, as follows:

$$(a - 1) + (ab - b),$$

the terms of which can be regrouped as

$$(a + ab) - (1 + b),$$

making it reasonable to say that the general effect of A is a comparison of the two columns of the 2×2 table. In either case, the combinations involving A are compared with those not involving A.

The general effect of B is defined by combining specific effects, $(b - 1)$ and $(ab - a)$. The expression of the combination can be rearranged as

$$(b + ab) - (1 + a),$$

indicating a comparison of the rows of the 2 × 2 table.

We have acknowledged that the two specific effects of A, $(a - 1)$ and $(ab - b)$, may differ. When they do, it can be said that the effect of A depends on the presence or absence of B. That is to say, the two variables, A and B, interact. The interaction effect is measured by the difference between the two specific effects, that is, by

$$(ab - b) - (a - 1),$$

which can be rewritten as

$$(ab + 1) - (a + b),$$

indicating a comparison of the two diagonals of the 2 × 2 table.

An interaction is usually identified by the letters of the variables involved. For example, the interaction of A and B is designated AB. There is only one interaction in the 2 × 2 treatment plan. The difference between the two specific effects of B,

$$(ab - a) - (b - 1)$$

can be rewritten as

$$(ab + 1) - (a + b),$$

indicating again a comparison of the diagonals.

The 2 × 2 treatment plan thus provides information concerning two main effects, A and B, and the interaction effect, AB.

It is worth noting that the expression for the main effect, A,

$$(a + ab) - (1 + b)$$

can be "factored", yielding

$$a(1 + b) - 1(1 + b),$$

which can be factored again, producing

$$(a - 1)(b + 1).$$

Factoring the expression for the main effect, B, in a similar fashion, yields

$$(a + 1)(b - 1).$$

Factoring the expression for the interaction, AB, gives

$$(a - 1)(b - 1).$$

These factored expressions have a characteristic form which the student should be able to discern. They have no important meaning but, in more complex treatment plans, are very useful for working out desired comparisons in a systematic and efficient fashion.

It is also worthwhile to note that the interaction comparison can be expressed as a comparison of treatment combinations having an even number of letters in common with AB with those having an odd number of letters in common with AB.

Consider next a three-factor plan with two levels of each factor. The three factors or independent variables are $A, B,$ and C. The complete set of treatment combinations is given in Plan 11.2. Two 2×2 tables are needed to

		C_1			C_2	
	A_1	A_2			A_1	A_2
B_1	1	a		B_1	c	ac
B_2	b	ab		B_2	bc	abc

Plan 11.2   Three-factor treatment plan with two levels of each factor.

provide for the eight combinations of treatments. The scheme might be referred to as a $2 \times 2 \times 2$ or 2^3 plan.

There are four specific effects of A, given by the four comparisons:

$$a - 1,$$
$$ab - b,$$
$$ac - c,$$
$$abc - bc,$$

each of which varies only in the presence or absence of A.

The general or main effect of A is obtained by combining the four specific effects as follows:

$$(a - 1) + (ab - b) + (ac - c) + (abc - bc),$$

which can be rearranged as

$$a + ab + ac + abc - 1 - b - c - bc,$$

indicating a comparison of columns labeled A_2 with those labeled A_1, or a comparison of treatments involving A with those not involving A.

The general effect of B is obtained by combining the four specific effects:

$$b - 1,$$
$$ab - a,$$
$$bc - c,$$
$$abc - ac.$$

The resulting expression can be rewritten as

$$b + ab + bc + abc - 1 - a - c - ac,$$

indicating a comparison of rows labeled B_2 with rows labeled B_1, or a comparison of treatments involving B with those not involving B.

The main effect C is obtained by combining

$$c - 1,$$
$$ac - a,$$
$$bc - b,$$
$$abc - ab,$$

yielding

$$c + ac + bc + abc - 1 - a - b - ab.$$

We go next to the interactions.

Note that we can write an interaction for A and B in the absence of C, and another for A and B in the presence of C. That is, the effects of A in the absence of C are

$$a - 1$$

and

$$ab - b.$$

The difference between these two specific effects,

$$(ab - b) - (a - 1),$$

is the interaction AB in the absence of C.   The effects of A in the presence of C are

$$ac - c$$

and

$$abc - bc.$$

The difference between these two specific effects,

$$(abc - bc) - (ac - c),$$

is the interaction AB in the presence of C.

The general interaction AB is obtained by combining the two specific interactions, as follows:

$$(ab - b) - (a - 1) + (abc - bc) - (ac - c),$$

which can be rewritten as

$$1 + c + ab + abc - a - b - ac - bc.$$

The interaction can be described by reference to the two 2×2 tables of Plan 11.2.   Treatments in corresponding diagonals of the tables are grouped together and the two groups are then compared.

In a similar fashion, the interaction AC combines the two specific interactions

$$(abc - bc) - (ab - b)$$

and

$$(ac - c) - (a - 1),$$

and can be written finally as

$$1 + b + ac + abc - a - c - ab - bc.$$

Treatments in noncorresponding columns of the two tables in Plan 11.2 are grouped together and the two groups are then compared.

The interaction BC can be written as

$$1 + a + bc + abc - b - c - ab - ac,$$

which indicates that treatments in noncorresponding rows of the tables are to be grouped together.

An interaction involving two variables is called a *first-order* interaction. There are three such interactions in the $2 \times 2 \times 2$ treatment plan: AB, AC, and BC.

One more effect remains to be defined in the three-factor plan. Recall that the interaction AB was obtained by combining two specific interactions,

$$(ab - b) - (a - 1)$$

and

$$(abc - bc) - (ac - c).$$

The difference between these specific interactions defines the *second-order* interaction ABC. In writing the difference between these two differences between differences, one must be careful of changes in signs. With parentheses removed, signs changed, and terms regrouped, the comparison for the second-order interaction ABC becomes

$$a + b + c + abc - 1 - ab - ac - bc.$$

In the tables of Plan 11.2, the treatments of noncorresponding diagonals are grouped together, and the two resulting groups are then compared.

The $2 \times 2 \times 2$ treatment plan thus provides information concerning three main effects, three first-order interactions, and one second-order interaction. They are listed below. The expressions defining each effect have also been listed, in factored form:

A	$(a - 1)(b + 1)(c + 1)$
B	$(a + 1)(b - 1)(c + 1)$
C	$(a + 1)(b + 1)(c - 1)$
AB	$(a - 1)(b - 1)(c + 1)$
AC	$(a - 1)(b + 1)(c - 1)$
BC	$(a + 1)(b - 1)(c - 1)$
ABC	$(a - 1)(b - 1)(c - 1)$

Another convenient device for writing interaction comparisons is the rule, mentioned earlier in the two-factor plan, concerning odd and even numbers of letters. In writing any given interaction comparison, the treatments can be grouped according to whether the number of letters they have in common with the interaction is odd or even.

Having examined the experimental comparisons which factorial designs make possible, we are now in a position to assess their importance to the experimenter. The advantage of factorial designs is that they provide information which is not available from single-variable designs. The generality of the effect produced by a given treatment, as it is measured by a main effect, is important information. It has been said that the single variable experiment is artificially simple. Practical situations outside the laboratory are often subject to the influence of combinations of variables. The effect of a treatment over a variety of situations is of greater interest than its effect in a single isolated situation. Furthermore, the specificity of the effects of a given treatment is not lost in a factorial design. The variation in the effect of a treatment over a variety of other conditions is measured by the interaction. Thus, how much the difference produced by one condition depends on the presence in some degree of another condition is available information. The traditional experiment in which a single variable is manipulated and all others held constant may not tell us what we need to know about the complex real world in terms of the generality and the specificity of treatment effects.

There is a circumstance in which the meaningfulness of the main effect can be questioned. The main effect is an average of two or more specific effects. When the differences among the specific effects are real, we say there is an interaction. Even though the specific effects do exhibit real variation, it may be of interest to know what we can expect in general or on the average. A problem arises when the several specific effects are so varied as to be inconsistent or contradictory. It is possible for a given treatment to have a real effect when combined with a particular level of another variable and no effect when combined with a different level of the other variable. It is even possible, at least theoretically, for a given treatment to have opposite effects in the two instances. For example, in the two-factor plan, the effect of A in the absence of B, as given by the comparison $(a - 1)$ may be $+5$ units, while the effect of A in the presence of B, as given by the comparison $(ab - b)$ may be -3 units. What does it mean to say that the general effect of A is $+2$ units, which is the result of combining the two specific effects, or, what is equivalent, that the average of the two effects is $+1$ unit? To speak of the general effect when the specific effects are so discrepant is not meaningful. In actual practice, the problem of interpretation may not be serious. Widely discrepant effects may be the exception rather than the rule in most research, including psychological experimentation.

Treatment plans are not limited to squares and cubes with two levels for each variable. Many variations are possible. For example, a 2×3 arrangement is presented in Plan 11.3. With three levels of A, the combi-

	A_1	A_2	A_3
B_1	a_1b_1	a_2b_1	a_3b_1
B_2	a_1b_2	a_2b_2	a_3b_2

Plan 11.3 Two-factor treatment plan in which the number of levels varies.

nation notation is modified. The main effect B is obtained by combining the three specific effects

$$a_1b_2 - a_1b_1,$$
$$a_2b_2 - a_2b_1,$$
$$a_3b_2 - a_3b_1,$$

The variation in these three specific effects is the interaction AB. The main effect A involves a comparison of the three columns or the differences among the three combinations

$$a_1b_2 + a_1b_1,$$
$$a_2b_2 + a_2b_1,$$
$$a_3b_2 + a_3b_1.$$

The comparisons for A can be written more formally and specifically but will be deferred for presentation in a later chapter.

ARRANGEMENT OF SUBJECTS

A factorial experiment requires a treatment plan and a number of subjects arranged usually in either random samples or matched groups. It will be less complicated to begin the discussion with an arrangement of random samples and no adjusting variable. Factorial designs with matched groups will be presented in Chapter 12. Factorial designs with adjusting will be described in Chapter 13.

The 2×2 plan given in Plan 11.1 requires four samples of n subjects. Samples are randomly assigned one to each of the four treatment combinations: 1, *a*, *b*, and *ab*. Treatments are imposed and measures on the dependent variable are obtained. The experimental data consist, then, of $N = 4n$ observations.

Variability in the N observations can be analyzed into components. The analysis can be considered in two stages. In the first stage, the total sum of squares is separated into two components: the sum of squares for differences among the four samples and the sum of squares for differences within the four samples.

When treatment effects are constant and additive, they will be contained in the differences among samples. The within-sample variability, then, contains only error.

The total sum of squares for the $N = 4n$ observations can be obtained by formula (4.2),

$$\Sigma Y^2 - C'.$$

The summation involves $N = 4n$ terms.

The within-sample sum of squares is computed by applying, to each sample, formula (4.1):

$$\Sigma Y^2 - \frac{(\Sigma Y)^2}{n}.$$

The summation involves n terms. The four sums of squares are then combined.

We could display the between-sample differences by eliminating within-sample differences. Substituting the mean of a sample for each value in the sample would eliminate the variability in that sample. The between-sample sum of squares could be computed from the resulting values or from the four sample means, but it is much more convenient to use sample sums.

Let 1, *a*, *b*, and *ab* be sample sums. Then the between-sample component is given by an adaptation of formula (4.3)

$$\frac{(1^2 + a^2 + b^2 + ab^2)}{n} - C'$$

or, if we let S be any sample sum, we can write the formula as

$$\frac{\Sigma S^2}{n} - C'.$$

The second stage of the analysis is the subdivision of the between-sample sum of squares into three parts: two main effects, A and B, and the interaction, AB. The sum of squares for A could be obtained from the mean of samples under A_1 and the mean of samples under A_2, but again it is much more convenient to use sums. Up to this point, the symbols A_1 and A_2 have only designated levels of treatment variable A, but we can make additional good use of them as sums. That is, let

$$A_1 = 1 + b,$$
$$A_2 = a + ab,$$

where 1, a, b, and ab are the four sample sums. Then the A component is

$$\frac{(A_1^2 + A_2^2)}{2n} - C'$$

or

$$\frac{\Sigma A^2}{2n} - C',$$

both of which are adaptations of formula (4.3).

If we let

$$B_1 = 1 + a,$$
$$B_2 = b + ab,$$

then the sum of squares for B is

$$\frac{(B_1^2 + B_2^2)}{2n} - C'$$

or

$$\frac{\Sigma B^2}{2n} - C'.$$

The sum of squares for the first-order interaction AB is computed from the diagonal sums which group the observations as $(1 + ab)$ and $(a + b)$. The formula is

$$\frac{(ab + 1)^2 + (a + b)^2}{2n} - C'.$$

If we let

$$D_1 = ab + 1,$$
$$D_2 = a + b,$$

then the interaction sum of squares becomes

$$\frac{(D_1^2 + D_2^2)}{2n} - C'$$

or

$$\frac{\Sigma D^2}{2n} - C'.$$

In summary, the between-sample sum of squares can be subdivided into three components representing apparent treatment effects: *A*, *B*, and *AB*. The within-sample sum of squares is a measure of error.

Variances can be computed for these four components by dividing each component by an appropriate number of degrees of freedom. Three tests of significance are possible. *F* for each test is the ratio of a treatment variance to the error variance. Table 11.1 shows the general form of the conventional presentation of results.

Table 11.1

ANALYSIS OF VARIANCE FOR A 2 × 2 DESIGN

Component	df	V	F
A	1	V_a	V_a/V_e
B	1	V_b	V_b/V_e
AB	1	V_{ab}	V_{ab}/V_e
Error	$4(n-1)$	V_e	
Total	$N-1$		

n = number of subjects per sample
$N = 4n$ = total number of subjects

The $2 \times 2 \times 2$ treatment plan of Plan 11.2 requires eight samples. Variability in the $N = 8n$ observations can be analyzed into two components: the between-sample sum of squares and the within-sample sum of squares. The between-sample sum of squares can then be analyzed into components for three main effects, three first-order interactions, and one second-order interaction.

The total sum of squares for the $N = 8n$ observations can be computed by formula (4.2),

$$\Sigma Y^2 - C',$$

where the summation has $N = 8n$ terms.

The within-sample sum of squares is obtained by computing eight sums of squares, one for each sample, and then combining them. Formula (4.1) for the sum of squares of a single sample is

$$\Sigma Y^2 - \frac{(\Sigma Y)^2}{n},$$

where the summation involves n terms.

If we let 1, a, b, c, ab, ac, bc, and abc be sample sums, then the between-sample sum of squares is obtained by a variation of formula (4.3),

$$\frac{(1^2 + a^2 + b^2 + c^2 + ab^2 + ac^2 + bc^2 + abc^2)}{n} - C'$$

or, if we let S be any sample sum, we can write

$$\frac{\Sigma S^2}{n} - C'.$$

If we then let

$$
\begin{aligned}
A_1 &= 1 + b + c + bc, \\
A_2 &= a + ab + ac + abc, \\
B_1 &= 1 + a + c + ac, \\
B_2 &= b + ab + bc + abc, \\
C_1 &= 1 + a + b + ab, \\
C_2 &= c + ac + bc + abc, \\
AB_1 &= a + b + ac + bc, \\
AB_2 &= 1 + c + ab + abc, \\
AC_1 &= a + c + ab + bc, \\
AC_2 &= 1 + b + ac + abc, \\
BC_1 &= b + c + ab + ac, \\
BC_2 &= 1 + a + bc + abc, \\
ABC_1 &= 1 + ab + ac + bc, \\
ABC_2 &= a + b + c + abc,
\end{aligned}
$$

the seven treatment effects can be computed as follows:

$$A: \quad \frac{\Sigma A^2}{4n} - C',$$

$$B: \quad \frac{\Sigma B^2}{4n} - C',$$

$$C: \quad \frac{\Sigma C^2}{4n} - C',$$

$$AB: \quad \frac{\Sigma (AB)^2}{4n} - C',$$

$$AC: \quad \frac{\Sigma (AC)^2}{4n} - C',$$

$$BC: \quad \frac{\Sigma (BC)^2}{4n} - C',$$

$$ABC: \quad \frac{\Sigma (ABC)^2}{4n} - C'.$$

Note that each summation involves just two terms, the squares of the sums of two groups of observations.   Note also that these seven formulas are only adaptations of formula (4.3).

Degrees of freedom for computing the seven treatment variances and the error variance are given in Table 11.2.   The variance ratios for the seven tests of significance of the seven treatment effects are also indicated in Table 11.2.

Table 11.2
ANALYSIS OF VARIANCE OF A 2 × 2 × 2 DESIGN

Component	df	V	F
A	1	V_a	V_a/V_e
B	1	V_b	V_b/V_e
C	1	V_c	V_c/V_e
AB	1	V_{ab}	V_{ab}/V_e
AC	1	V_{ac}	V_{ac}/V_e
BC	1	V_{bc}	V_{bc}/V_e
ABC	1	V_{abc}	V_{abc}/V_e
Error	$8(n-1)$	V_e	
Total	$N-1$		

n = number of subjects per sample
$N = 8n$ = total number of subjects

A design having two levels for every independent variable can be characterized as a 2^h plan, where h is the number of independent variables or factors, 2 is the number of levels, and the quantity 2^h is the number of treatment combinations in the design.   In 2^h designs, all main effects and interactions can be computed by the same general procedures.   The observations are divided into two groups, defined by the treatment effect in question.   The sum of each group of observations is obtained.   Let us say that G_1 and G_2 are the two group sums.   Then the formula for any treatment component is

$$\frac{(G_1^2 + G_2^2)}{m} - C'$$

or

$$\frac{\Sigma G^2}{m} - C',$$

where $m = N/2$.

Plan 11.4 gives a 3 × 3 treatment plan, that is, one having two independent variables and three levels of each variable.   Nine samples of subjects would be required for an experiment. Each sample would be randomly assigned to one of the nine combinations of treatments in the plan.

	A_1	A_2	A_3
B_1	a_1b_1	a_2b_1	a_3b_1
B_2	a_1b_2	a_2b_2	a_3b_2
B_3	a_1b_3	a_2b_3	a_3b_3

Plan 11.4   A two-factor treatment plan involving three levels of each factor.

The total variability in the $N = 9n$ observations would be computed by formula (4.2),
$$\Sigma Y^2 - C',$$
where the summation involves $N = 9n$ terms.

Formula (4.1) for the sum of squares for a single sample is
$$\Sigma Y^2 - \frac{(\Sigma Y)^2}{n},$$
where the summations have n terms.   Having obtained a sum of squares for each sample, we would combine the nine quantities into the within-sample sum of squares, a measure of error.

If we let S be the sum of any one of the nine samples, then the between-sample sum of squares could be obtained by a variant of formula (4.3)
$$\frac{\Sigma S^2}{n} - C',$$
where the summation involves nine squared sample sums.

The between-sample sum of squares can be subdivided into three components: two main effects, A and B, and one first-order interaction, AB.   If we let A be any column sum in Plan 11.4, then a variant of formula (4.3),
$$\frac{\Sigma A^2}{3n} - C',$$
is the sum of squares for the main effect A.   Likewise, if we let B represent any row sum, then
$$\frac{\Sigma B^2}{3n} - C'$$
will give the sum of squares for B.

Computation of the interaction sum of squares requires some preliminary discussion. The nine samples in a design employing Plan 11.4 have already been classified in two different ways, by columns and by rows. The main effect A is computed from column sums. B is computed from row sums. It would be helpful if we could classify the nine samples in some additional way and compute the interaction sum of squares from these new class sums. We can do so, but it actually turns out that we must reclassify twice, not just once.

The 3×3 *Greco-Latin square* is the device which determines or guides the reclassification. A 3×3 Latin square results from assigning three different Latin letters to the cells of a 3×3 table according to a certain principle: that each different letter shall appear once and only once in each row and column. A Greco-Latin square results from assigning three different Greek letters to the cells of a Latin square according to the same principle, but with one additional requirement: that each different Greek letter shall appear once and only once with each different Latin letter. We might refer to the Latin square as a square in one alphabet and to the Greco-Latin square as a square in two alphabets. In squares larger than 3×3, the principle can be extended to the assigning of three and more alphabets. It is convenient, in writing squares, to use numerals instead of letters and to distinguish between "alphabets" by the positions given the numerals in each cell of the table.

Let us agree that the first alphabet will consist of the three numerals: 1, 2, and 3, placed in the left position in each cell; and that the second alphabet will be the same three numerals placed in the right position. A square in two alphabets is shown in Table 11.3. Each alphabet provides the means of

Table 11.3

A 3 $\times$ 3 SQUARE IN TWO ALPHABETS

3 1	2 2	1 3
2 3	1 1	3 2
1 2	3 3	2 1

classifying the nine cells of the 3×3 table into three groups. If we pay attention only to the first alphabet, that is, to the numeral on the left in each cell, then we see that the cells can be classified as 1's, 2's, and 3's, there being three of each. If we pay attention only to the second alphabet, the numeral on the right, then the cells are again classifiable as 1's, 2's, and 3's.

Imagine that Table 11.3 is superimposed on Plan 11.4. The nine treatment combinations of Plan 11.4 can now be classified according to the first alphabet and the corresponding sample sums can be combined in the following manner:

$$(1\text{'s}): a_1b_3 + a_2b_2 + a_3b_1 = P_1,$$
$$(2\text{'s}): a_1b_2 + a_2b_1 + a_3b_3 = P_2,$$
$$(3\text{'s}): a_1b_1 + a_2b_3 + a_3b_2 = P_3.$$

A sum of squares can be computed for this new classification. The formula, which requires the class sums, P_1, P_2, and P_3, is

$$\frac{\Sigma P^2}{3n} - C'.$$

The nine sample sums of Plan 11.4 can be reclassified again, according to the second alphabet and combined as shown below.

$$(1\text{'s}): a_1b_1 + a_2b_2 + a_3b_3 = Q_1,$$
$$(2\text{'s}): a_1b_3 + a_2b_1 + a_3b_2 = Q_2,$$
$$(3\text{'s}): a_1b_2 + a_2b_3 + a_3b_1 = Q_3.$$

A sum of squares can be computed from the Q's. The formula takes the familiar form

$$\frac{\Sigma Q^2}{3n} - C'.$$

The sums of squares for the two alphabets together constitute the interaction sum of squares. For convenience, let us call these two components P and Q. The complete analysis of the 3×3 design is presented in Table 11.4.

Table 11.4
ANALYSIS FOR A 3×3 DESIGN WITH RANDOM SAMPLES

Component	df	V	F
A	2	V_a	V_a/V_e
B	2	V_b	V_b/V_e
AB	4	V_{ab}	V_{ab}/V_e
P	2		
Q	2		
Error	$9(n-1)$	V_e	
Total	$N-1$		

P = classification by first alphabet
Q = classification by second alphabet
n = number of subjects per sample
$N = 9n$ = total number of subjects

AN EXAMPLE

Data from a 2 × 3 design are presented in Table 11.5. In the table are scores on an arithmetic test administered to six random samples of freshman engineering students at a state university. Scores on the six samples were

Table 11.5
DATA FOR A TWO-FACTOR EXPERIMENT ON SLEEP AND FOOD DEPRIVATION

Hours of Sleep Deprivation

		16 A_1	20 A_2	24 A_3
12	B_1	93 107 108 98 99	114 98 104 92 112	82 97 81 89 96
18	B_2	113 100 102 115 115	95 96 92 108 109	90 102 103 89 101

Hours of
Food
Deprivation

obtained under six different combinations of conditions involving three levels of sleep deprivation: 16, 20 and 24 hours; and two levels of food deprivation: 12 and 18 hours.

Variability in the $N = 6n = 30$ arithmetic test scores can be analyzed into four components: three treatment effects and an estimate of error. The total sum of squares can be computed by the formula

$$\Sigma Y^2 - C'$$

$$302,530 - (3000)^2/30 = 2530$$

The sum of squares for a single sample is computed by the formula

$$\Sigma Y^2 - \frac{(\Sigma Y)^2}{n}.$$

The six sample sums of squares are given in Table 11.6. Combined they give an error sum of squares of 1390. That is,

$$162 + 218 + 344 + 250 + 226 + 190 = 1390$$

Table 11.6

SUMMARY DATA FOR THE SLEEP AND FOOD DEPRIVATION EXPERIMENT

Within-Sample Sums of Squares

	A_1	A_2	A_3
B_1	162	344	226
B_2	218	250	190

Sample Means

	A_1	A_2	A_3	Row Means
B_1	101	104	89	98
B_2	109	100	97	102
Column Means	105	102	93	100 = Total Mean

Interaction Deviations

	A_1	A_2	A_3
B_1	-2	$+4$	-2
B_2	$+2$	-4	$+2$

The sum of squares for the differences among the six samples is obtained by

$$\frac{\Sigma S^2}{n} - C',$$

where S is any sample sum and the summation involves six terms. Substituting the sample sums, we have

$$(505^2 + 545^2 + 520^2 + 500^2 + 445^2 + 485^2)/5 - 300,000 = 1140,$$

which can be subdivided into three components: $A, B,$ and AB.

The sum of squares for A is given by

$$\frac{\Sigma A^2}{2n} - C',$$

$$(1050^2 + 1020^2 + 930^2)/10 - 300,000 = 780.$$

For B we have

$$\frac{\Sigma B^2}{3n} - C',$$

$$(1470^2 + 1530^2)/15 - 300,000 = 120.$$

Only the interaction sum of squares remains to be found. The computing methods described previously, however, cannot be applied here. The method we shall use requires computation of the total mean, the means of rows and columns, and the sample means. These values are displayed in Table 11.6. The formula for the interaction deviation for any sample mean is

$$(\bar{Y}_{jk} - \bar{Y}_{.k} - \bar{Y}_{j.} + \bar{Y}_{..}) \tag{11.1}$$

or, in words, "the sample mean minus the mean of the column, minus the mean of the row, plus the total mean." The interaction deviations are also displayed in Table 11.6. To compute the interaction sum of squares, we square each interaction deviation, multiply each squared deviation by n, and sum these products. We find the sum of squares for AB in the example to be 240.

Formula 11.1 is obtained from the following expression, which defines an interaction deviation as

$$(\bar{Y}_{jk} - \bar{Y}_{..}) - (\bar{Y}_{.k} - \bar{Y}_{..}) - (\bar{Y}_{j.} - \bar{Y}_{..})$$

or, in words, the part remaining in the deviation of a sample mean from the total mean, after removing the general effect of both treatments in the treatment combination.

Table 11.7 shows the results of the analysis of variance. Only the effects of sleep deprivation are significant. Performance on the test declines as the number of hours of sleep deprivation increases.

Table 11.7
ANALYSIS OF VARIANCE FOR DATA IN TABLE 11.5

Component	SS	df	V	F
Sleep deprivation	780	2	390	6.73*
Food deprivation	120	1	120	2.07
Interaction	240	2	120	2.07
Error	1390	24	57.92	
Total	2530	29		

F_c, the criterion at the 0.05 level for 2 and 24 df is 3.40; for 1 and 24 df, it is 4.26

* Null hypothesis rejected

It is appropriate to test for homogeneity of sample variances. Bartlett's test is applied below. (See the outline of steps in computation on pages 59 and 60.)

$$V_w = 1390/24 = 57.92,$$

$$(N - 6)\log V_w = 24(1.7628) = 42.31.$$

The logarithms of the six sample variances are listed below:

$$\log 40.5 = 1.6075,$$
$$\log 86.0 = 1.9345,$$
$$\log 56.5 = 1.7520,$$
$$\log 54.5 = 1.7364,$$
$$\log 62.5 = 1.7959,$$
$$\log 47.5 = 1.6767,$$
$$\Sigma \log V_{jk} = 10.5030.$$

where V_{jk} is the sample variance in the jth row and kth column of the 2×3 table.

$$(n - 1)\Sigma \log V_{jk} = 4(10.5030) = 42.01,$$
$$D = 42.31 - 42.01 = 0.30,$$
$$E = 1.10,$$
$$f = 2.3026/1.10 = 2.09,$$
$$\chi^2 = fD = 2.09(.30) = 0.63.$$

Since the criterion value of chi square for the 0.05 level of significance and 5 degrees of freedom is 11.07, the null hypothesis is accepted and the assumption of additive treatment effects is considered justified. (See Table C in the Appendix for the criterion value of chi square.)

PERSPECTIVE

In theory, factorial designs may have any number of factors with any number of levels. In practice, in psychological research, two-factor and three-factor designs are used most widely. Occasionally there is need for a more comprehensive design. Designs with three or more factors are often difficult to manage. In addition, the third and higher order interactions probably have little practical significance.

Sources of variability and degrees of freedom for the general two-factor design are given in Table 11.8. The number of levels for the one factor, A, is n_a. The number of levels for the other factor, B, is n_b.

Table 11.8

COMPONENTS AND DEGREES OF FREEDOM IN THE GENERAL TWO-FACTOR DESIGN WITH RANDOM SAMPLES

Component	df
A	$n_a - 1$,
B	$n_b - 1$,
AB	$(n_a - 1)(n_b - 1)$,
Error	$n_a n_b(n - 1)$,
Total	$N - 1$.

n_a = number of levels of A
n_b = number of levels of B
n = number of subjects per sample
$N = n_a n_b n$ = total number of subjects

Sources of variability and degrees of freedom for the general three-factor design are shown in Table 11.9. The number of levels for A is n_a; for B, it is n_b; and for C, it is n_c.

Table 11.9

COMPONENTS AND DEGREES OF FREEDOM IN THE GENERAL THREE-FACTOR DESIGN WITH RANDOM SAMPLES

Component	df
A	$n_a - 1$
B	$n_b - 1$
C	$n_c - 1$
AB	$(n_a - 1)(n_b - 1)$
AC	$(n_a - 1)(n_c - 1)$
BC	$(n_b - 1)(n_c - 1)$
ABC	$(n_a - 1)(n_b - 1)(n_c - 1)$
Error	$n_a n_b n_c(n - 1)$
Total	$N - 1$

n_a = number of levels of A
n_b = number of levels of B
n_c = number of levels of C
n = number of subjects per sample
$N = n_a n_b n_c n$ = total number of subjects

The computation of sums of squares for first and second order interactions in the general three-factor design merits additional explanation.

One would begin by computing sums of squares for the three main effects in the usual fashion.

Any first-order interaction is then computed as follows:

1. Classify all observations into a single two-dimensional table where columns represent levels of one factor in the particular interaction and rows represent levels of the other factor. (The third factor is not used in the classifying.)

2. Find the sum for each cell.

3. Compute the sum of squares for differences between cells by summing the squares of the cell sums, dividing by the number of observations in each cell and subtracting the correction term.

4. Compute the interaction sum of squares by subtracting the main effects for rows and columns from the quantity obtained in step 3 above.

The second-order interaction is then computed as follows:

1. Find the sum of squares for differences between samples by summing the squares of sample sums, dividing the sum by the number of observations per sample, and subtracting the correction term from this quotient.

2. Compute the second-order interaction sum of squares by subtracting the three main effects and the three first-order interactions from the between sample sum of squares obtained in step 1, immediately preceding.

When an experiment is to be performed in which the three factors, A, B, and C, do not interact, a treatment plan based on the Latin-square principle makes very efficient use of subjects. If one wished to experiment with two levels of each of three treatments, one could combine treatments as shown in Plan 11.5. Each cell is a sample. Although the plan accommodates three factors, only four samples are required. The components of variability and

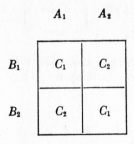

Plan 11.5 A treatment plan accommodating two levels of each of three factors. The plan incorporates the Latin-square principle in the assignment of levels of C.

degrees of freedom are listed in Table 11.10. Notice that the comparison for main effect C corresponds to the AB interaction in the 2×2 design. The Latin square could obviously not be used if there was any interaction between A and B. The AB interaction would be confounded with the main

Table 11.10
ANALYSIS FOR A THREE-FACTOR 2×2 LATIN-SQUARE DESIGN

Component	df
A	1
B	1
C	1
Error	$4(n - 1)$
Total	$N - 1$

n = number of subjects per sample
$N = 4n$ = total number of subjects

effect C and the two could not be separated. For the same reason, the other interactions, AC, BC and ABC, must also not exist.

The 3×3 Greco-Latin square of Plan 11.6 could guide the assignment of treatments to nine samples. The square accommodates three levels of each

	A_1	A_2	A_3
B_1	C_1D_3	C_2D_2	C_3D_1
B_2	C_3D_2	C_1D_1	C_2D_3
B_3	C_2D_1	C_3D_3	C_1D_2

Plan 11.6 A treatment plan accommodating three levels of each of four factors. The plan incorporates the Greco-Latin square principle in the assignment of levels of C and levels of D.

of four factors: A, B, C, and D. The four main effects, each associated with two degrees of freedom, would account for the eight degrees of freedom for the differences among the nine samples. Here again the treatment plan would be inappropriate if any of the factors interacted.   The general form of the analysis is given in Table 11.11.

Table 11.11
ANALYSIS FOR A FOUR-FACTOR 3×3 GRECO-LATIN SQUARE DESIGN

Component	df
A	2
B	2
C	2
D	2
Error	$9(n-1)$
Total	$N-1$

n = number of subjects per sample
$N = 9n$ = total number of subjects

For a more complete discussion of the issues which arise in the use of Latin squares in psychological research, see Grant[1] and McNemar.[2]

No attention has yet been given in our discussion to matching and adjusting in factorial designs These topics will be considered in the next two chapters.   Factorial designs would very likely be lacking in precision if no matching or adjusting was done.   The probability of errors of the second kind would be higher than necessary.   Real differences would go undetected in many instances.

REFERENCES

1. Grant, D.A., "The Latin Square Principle in the Design and Analysis of Psychological Experiments," *Psychological Bulletin*, 45, 1948, 427–442.
2. McNemar, Q., "On the Use of Latin Squares in Psychology," *Psychological Bulletin*, 48, 1951, 398–401.

FACTORIAL DESIGNS
WITH MATCHING

12

Let us briefly review the matched-group design for single-variable experiments. When two levels of a single independent variable are employed, the matched group is a pair. The selection of two subjects for any pair is guided by the ranks of measures obtained under uniform conditions prior to the experiment. The greater the correlation between the matching variable, X, and the dependent variable, Y, the more homogeneous the members of each pair will be. In general, when c levels of the independent variable are used, the matched group consists of c subjects.

Now let us turn to the matching procedures for factorial designs. In a factorial design, the number of subjects in a matched group is determined by the number of combinations of treatments prescribed by the design. One combination of treatments is applied to each subject in a group. A complete set of comparisons is then possible within each homogeneous group of subjects. The magnitude of residual errors, that is, inequalities not completely eliminated by the matching, can be estimated from the variation in the comparisons from one matched group to another.

TWO FACTORS

In the 2×2 design, four combinations of treatments are necessary for the evaluation of two main effects and one first order interaction. One subject in each matched group must be assigned to each treatment combination. Consequently, a matched group consists of four subjects. Any number of matched groups might be employed, depending on the availability of subjects for experimentation.

162

In the experiment, the psychologist obtains a sample of subjects. He measures all subjects under uniform conditions on a matching variable, X, that is known to be correlated with the dependent variable, Y. He ranks the subjects on the matching measure and then forms matched groups of four individuals in the usual manner by taking the four with the highest ranks for the first group, the four with the next highest ranks for the second group, and so on. Next, he randomly assigns the four subjects in each group to the four combinations of treatments, after which he imposes the treatments and measures the subjects' responses. A general arrangement of subjects, treatment combinations, and observations for the 2 × 2 design is given in Table 12.1.

Table 12.1
THE GENERAL ARRANGEMENT OF SUBJECTS, CONDITIONS, AND OBSERVATIONS IN THE 2 × 2 DESIGN WITH *r* MATCHED GROUPS

Treatment Combinations

		1	*a*	*b*	*ab*
	1	Y_{11}	Y_{12}	Y_{13}	Y_{14}
	2	Y_{21}	Y_{22}	Y_{23}	Y_{24}
Matched	·	·	·	·	·
Groups	*j*	Y_{j1}	Y_{j2}	Y_{j3}	Y_{j4}
	·	·	·	·	·
	r	Y_{r1}	Y_{r2}	Y_{r3}	Y_{r4}

Rows of the rectangle in Table 12.1 correspond to matched groups. Columns correspond to the treatment combinations placed above them. Each cell may be thought of as a subject. One measure is obtained and tabulated for the subject in that cell. The four subjects in each row are randomly assigned to the positions they occupy before treatments are imposed.

As a first step in analyzing the results, the total variability in the 2×2, matched-group design can be subdivided into three components. One component corresponds to the differences among columns and represents a measure of the treatment effects. When treatment effects are constant and additive, they will be contained in and limited to the between-column variability. A second component corresponds to differences among rows or matched groups and represents variability produced by the matching. A third component is the residual variability, a measure of error.

The total sum of squares can be obtained by the formula

$$\Sigma Y^2 - C'$$

where the summation has $4r$ terms.

If we let G be the sum of four observations on any matched group, then the between-row sum of squares is found by

$$\frac{\Sigma G^2}{4} - C',$$

where the summation has as many terms as there are matched groups.

If we let the column or treatment sums be represented by 1, a, b, and ab, then the between-column sum of squares or apparent treatment effect is given by

$$\frac{(1^2 + a^2 + b^2 + ab^2)}{r} - C',$$

where r is the number of matched groups.

The error sum of squares is computed by obtaining a residual deviation for each cell, squaring these deviations and summing the squares. A residual deviation, r_{jk}, is computed by formula (9.1), which is

$$r_{jk} = Y_{jk} - \bar{Y}_{j.} - \bar{Y}_{.k} + \bar{Y}_{..},$$

where j denotes any row or matched group and k denotes any column or treatment combination.

The second step in the analysis is to subdivide the treatment sum of squares into the two main effects, A and B, and the interaction, AB.

If we continue to regard 1, a, b, and ab as column sums, then the main effect A is derived from two groupings of the sums, those involving a and those not involving a. The computation is

$$\frac{(a + ab)^2 + (1 + b)^2}{2r} - C'.$$

If we let $a + ab = A_2$ and $1 + b = A_1$, the formula can be written more simply as

$$\frac{\Sigma A^2}{2r} - C'.$$

The main effect B is obtained from two groupings of the sums, those involving and those not involving b. The computation is

$$\frac{(b + ab)^2 + (1 + a)^2}{2r} - C'.$$

If we use B_2 for the combination having b and B_1 for the combination not having b, we can write

$$\frac{\Sigma B^2}{2r} - C'.$$

The interaction AB can be obtained by grouping the sums as indicated in the expression

$$\frac{(1 + ab)^2 + (a + b)^2}{2r} - C',$$

or, letting $D_1 = 1 + ab$ and $D_2 = a + b$, we could write

$$\frac{\Sigma D^2}{2r} - C'.$$

An outline of the analysis of variance for a 2×2 matched-group design with r matched groups is given in Table 12.2.

Table 12.2

ANALYSIS OF VARIANCE FOR THE 2×2 MATCHED-GROUP DESIGN

Component	df
A	1
B	1
AB	1
Error	$3(r - 1)$
Groups	$r - 1$
Total	$N - 1$

r = number of matched groups
$N = 4r$ = total number of subjects

Components of variability and degrees of freedom for the general two-factor, matched-group design are listed in Table 12.3.

Table 12.3
ANALYSIS OF VARIANCE FOR THE GENERAL TWO-FACTOR MATCHED-GROUP DESIGN

Component	df
A	$n_a - 1$
B	$n_b - 1$
AB	$(n_a - 1)(n_b - 1)$
Error	$(n_a n_b - 1)(r - 1)$
Groups	$r - 1$
Total	$N - 1$

n_a = number of levels of A
n_b = number of levels of B
r = number of matched groups
$N = n_a n_b r$ = total number of subjects

THREE FACTORS

The $2 \times 2 \times 2$ design defines eight combinations of treatments and requires, therefore, matched groups of eight subjects. Table 12.4 indicates the general arrangement of subjects, treatment combinations, and observations.

Table 12.4
THE GENERAL ARRANGEMENT OF SUBJECTS, TREATMENT COMBINATIONS, AND OBSERVATIONS IN THE $2 \times 2 \times 2$ DESIGN WITH r MATCHED GROUPS

Treatment Combinations

	1	a	b	c	ab	ac	bc	abc
1	Y_{11}	Y_{12}	Y_{13}	Y_{14}	Y_{15}	Y_{16}	Y_{17}	Y_{18}
2	Y_{21}	Y_{22}	Y_{23}	Y_{24}	Y_{25}	Y_{26}	Y_{27}	Y_{28}
Matched Groups $\cdot$	$\cdot$	$\cdot$	$\cdot$	$\cdot$	$\cdot$	$\cdot$	$\cdot$	$\cdot$
j	Y_{j1}	Y_{j2}	Y_{j3}	Y_{j4}	Y_{j5}	Y_{j6}	Y_{j7}	Y_{j8}
$\cdot$	$\cdot$	$\cdot$	$\cdot$	$\cdot$	$\cdot$	$\cdot$	$\cdot$	$\cdot$
r	Y_{r1}	Y_{r2}	Y_{r3}	Y_{r4}	Y_{r5}	Y_{r6}	Y_{r7}	Y_{r8}

The total variability in the $N = 8r$ measures can be analyzed into the three components: apparent treatment differences, differences between the matched groups, and the residual error. The apparent treatment differences can then be subdivided into three main effects, three first order interactions, and one second order interaction.

To compute the total sum of squares, we use

$$\Sigma Y^2 - C',$$

where the summation has $N = 8r$ terms.

The formula for the over-all treatment sum of squares is

$$\frac{1^2 + a^2 + b^2 + c^2 + ab^2 + ac^2 + bc^2 + abc^2}{r} - C',$$

where 1, a, b, etc. are sums of columns in Table 12.4.

A residual deviation is computed by formula (9.1),

$$r_{jk} = Y_{jk} - \bar{Y}_{j.} - \bar{Y}_{.k} + \bar{Y}_{..},$$

where jk denotes the cell in the jth row and kth column of Table 12.4. The residuals are squared and summed over the entire table, yielding the error sum of squares.

The over-all treatment sum of squares can be subdivided into seven treatment effects. We let

$$A_2 = a + ab + ac + abc,$$

$$A_1 = 1 + b + c + bc.$$

Then the main effect A is

$$\frac{\Sigma A^2}{4r} - C'$$

and, by analogy, the main effect B is

$$\frac{\Sigma B^2}{4r} - C'$$

and C is

$$\frac{\Sigma C^2}{4r} - C'.$$

If we let

$$AB_2 = 1 + c + ab + abc,$$
$$AB_1 = a + b + ac + bc,$$

then the sum of squares for the interaction AB is

$$\frac{\Sigma AB^2}{4r} - C'$$

and, by analogy, AC is

$$\frac{\Sigma AC^2}{4r} - C'.$$

The form of the computation should be generalized by the student to BC and ABC.

The analysis of variance for the $2 \times 2 \times 2$ matched-group design is given in Table 12.5. The analysis for the general three-factor, matched-group design takes the form of Table 12.6.

Table 12.5
ANALYSIS OF VARIANCE FOR THE
$2 \times 2 \times 2$ MATCHED-GROUP DESIGN

Component	df
A	1
B	1
C	1
AB	1
AC	1
BC	1
ABC	1
Error	$7(r - 1)$
Groups	$r - 1$
Total	$N - 1$

r = number of matched groups
$N = 8r$ = total number of observations

Table 12.6
ANALYSIS OF VARIANCE FOR THE GENERAL
THREE-FACTOR MATCHED-GROUP DESIGN

Component	df
A	$n_a - 1$
B	$n_b - 1$
C	$n_c - 1$
AB	$(n_a - 1)(n_b - 1)$
AC	$(n_a - 1)(n_c - 1)$
BC	$(n_b - 1)(n_c - 1)$
ABC	$(n_a - 1)(n_b - 1)(n_c - 1)$
Error	$(n_a n_b n_c - 1)(r - 1)$
Groups	$r - 1$
Total	$N - 1$

n_a = number of levels of A
n_b = number of levels of B
n_c = number of levels of C
r = number of matched groups
$N = n_a n_b n_c r$ = total number of subjects

AN EXAMPLE

A psychologist performed an experiment with a 2×2 matched-group design. Twenty randomly selected college students were tested under uniform conditions on a verbal analogies test. They were ranked and formed into five matched groups. The four subjects in each group were then randomly assigned to the treatment combinations 1, *a*, *b*, and *ab*, where levels of *A* were amounts of practice in solving verbal reasoning problems and levels of *B* were grades of difficulty in the practice materials. After the period of practice, the subjects were tested on verbal reasoning on new material and the number of problems each person solved in one hour was recorded as the dependent variable in the experiment. The scores are given in Table 12.7.

Table 12.7
DATA FOR EXPERIMENT ON VERBAL REASONING

Treatment Combinations

		1	a	b	ab
	1	14	13	12	17
Matched	2	10	9	13	12
Groups	3	8	10	9	13
	4	4	9	7	12
	5	4	4	9	11

Levels of *A:* amounts of practice
Levels of *B:* grades of difficulty in practice materials

The total sum of squares is

$$\Sigma Y^2 - C',$$

$$2230 - 2000 = 230.$$

The sum of squares for differences among groups is

$$\frac{\Sigma G^2}{4} - C',$$

$$\frac{8480}{4} - 2000 = 120.$$

The over-all treatment sum of squares is

$$\frac{1^2 + a^2 + b^2 + ab^2}{r} - C',$$

$$\frac{10,350}{5} - 2000 = 70.$$

The error sum of squares is the sum of the squares of the residual deviations, each of which is computed by formula (9.1),

$$\Sigma r_{jk}^2 = 40.$$

The main effect A is

$$\frac{(a + ab)^2 + (1 + b)^2}{2r} - C$$

or

$$\frac{\Sigma A^2}{2r} - C',$$

$$\frac{110^2 + 90^2}{10} - 2000 = 20.$$

B is

$$\frac{(b + ab)^2 + (1 + a)^2}{2r} - C'$$

or

$$\frac{\Sigma B^2}{2r} - C',$$

$$\frac{115^2 + 85^2}{10} - 2000 = 45.$$

AB is

$$\frac{(1 + ab)^2 + (a + b)^2}{2r} - C'$$

or

$$\frac{\Sigma D^2}{2r} - C',$$

$$\frac{105^2 + 95^2}{10} - 2000 = 5.$$

The results of the analysis for the verbal reasoning experiment are given in Table 12.8. The two main effects, practice and difficulty, were found to be significant. The interaction was not significant.

Table 12.8

ANALYSIS OF VARIANCE FOR THE DATA IN TABLE 12.7

Component	SS	df	V	F
Practice (A)	20	1	20	6.0*
Difficulty (B)	45	1	45	13.5*
Interaction (AB)	5	1	5	1.5
Error	40	12	3.33	
Groups	120	4		
Total	230	19		

F_c, the criterion value at the 0.05 level for 1 and 12 df is 4.75
* Null hypothesis rejected

INTENDED CONFOUNDING

If the number of subjects in the total sample is held constant, the precision of the matched-group design decreases as the size of the matched groups increases. For example, if there are 24 subjects in the total sample, the comparisons in a matched-pair design will be biased by smaller errors than the comparisons in a three-factor design employing matched groups of eight subjects. The reason for the smaller errors in the matched-pair design is that the heterogeneity of a pair will be less than the heterogeneity of a group of eight subjects when the same total group of subjects is subdivided.

There is a method by means of which the disadvantage of factorial designs in requiring large matched groups can be overcome to some extent, if the experimenter is willing to sacrifice information concerning one or more of the treatment effects. The method is known as *confounding*, a term which implies that two or more sources of variability are mixed together and cannot be separated. The method of intended confounding should not be confused with those instances of confounding which are unintended, which are the result of poor planning, and which often preclude a meaningful interpretation of the results. The experimenter can, if he so desires, deliberately constitute his groups of subjects and assign treatments to them so as to confound two or more components of variability. At the same time, as a consequence of the way in which his groups were constituted, he can evaluate certain selected treatment effects with greater precision.

Let us examine confounding as it may be carried out to advantage in the $2 \times 2 \times 2$ design. In the usual design, without confounding, a matched group consists of eight units of material. One matched group is employed for a single replication of the experiment. That is to say, the eight combinations of treatments are assigned randomly to the eight subjects in each matched group. All of the experimental comparisons among combinations of treatments can be made within a matched group.

Now, let us reduce the size of the matched group to four units. Each replication of the experiment will now require two matched groups of four subjects each instead of one matched group of eight. Four of the eight treatment combinations in a replication can be assigned randomly to the four subjects in one group. The other four combinations can be assigned randomly to the four subjects in a second group. Three complete replications, which originally required three matched groups of eight subjects each, now require six matched groups of four subjects.

Not all of the experimental comparisons can be made within the groups of four subjects. Any comparison of treatment combinations in different groups will contain, in addition to possible treatment effects, differences produced by the matching. Thus, treatment effects and differences between matched groups are confounded.

The experimenter can select a treatment effect, the evaluation of which he may be willing to sacrifice, and deliberately confound it with differences between groups. Suppose that he is willing to forego the evaluation of the second order interaction in the $2 \times 2 \times 2$ design. The comparison of treatment combinations for the interaction ABC, as we have seen previously, is

$$abc + a + b + c - ab - ac - bc - 1.$$

If we had eight subjects arranged in two groups, it is apparent that the two groups of subjects could be made to correspond to the two groupings in the ABC comparison given above. That is, four subjects in one group could be assigned to abc, a, b, and c. Four subjects in the other group could be assigned to ab, ac, bc, and 1.

The experimenter takes the following steps to deliberately confound the second order interaction with the differences among matched groups: He obtains a total sample of subjects. He measures all subjects under uniform conditions on a matching variable and ranks them. He then forms matched groups of four units. Two matched groups are selected for each replication. The four treatment combinations, abc, a, b and c, are assigned randomly to the four subjects in one group. The four combinations, ab, ac, bc and 1, are assigned randomly to the four subjects in a second group. The arrangement of subjects and treatments for a single replication is shown in Plan 12.1. Each cell is a subject. Each cluster of four cells is a matched group. In a complete design, the arrangement of Plan 12.1 would be repeated with additional subjects to provide as many replications as desired.

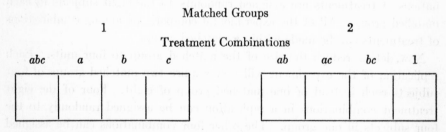

Matched Groups

1   2

Treatment Combinations

abc   *a*   *b*   *c*   *ab*   *ac*   *bc*   1

Plan 12.1 The arrangement of subjects and treatments necessary, in a single replication, for confounding the second order interaction ABC. Each cell is a subject.

Plan 12.1 shows that the comparison for the interaction ABC cannot be made within the matched groups. As a matter of fact, the ABC comparison is identical with a comparison of the two groups of subjects and, therefore, any second order interaction effect is confounded with the difference between the groups. The comparisons for the three main effects, A, B, and C, and the three first-order interactions, AB, AC, and BC, are independent of the ABC comparison and the corresponding difference between groups. That the comparison for a main effect or a first-order interaction can be built up of contrasts within the matched groups is apparent from an examination of the combinations of treatments involved in each case. The main effect A is given by the comparison

$$a + ab + ac + abc - 1 - b - c - bc$$

which can be expressed, in terms of contrasts within a group, as follows

$$(abc - b) + (a - c) + (ab - 1) + (ac - bc).$$

The first-order interaction AB is given by the comparison

$$abc + ab + c + 1 - a - b - ac - bc,$$

which can be expressed in terms of contrasts within both groups as

$$(abc - a) + (c - b) + (ab - ac) + (1 - bc).$$

Contrasts for the other main effects and first-order interactions can be shown in a similar manner.

Table 12.9 gives components of variability and degrees of freedom for a $2 \times 2 \times 2$ design with matched groups and confounding of the interaction

Table 12.9

**COMPONENTS OF VARIABILITY AND DEGREES OF FREEDOM
FOR THE $2 \times 2 \times 2$ DESIGN WITH CONFOUNDING**

Component	df
A	1
B	1
C	1
AB	1
AC	1
BC	1
Error	$6(u - 1)$
Groups	$2u - 1$
Total	$N - 1$

u = number of replications
$N = 8u$ = total number of subjects

ABC. The disadvantage of confounding in the 2 × 2 × 2 design is that information concerning the interaction *ABC* is not available. The advantage is that groups of four subjects can be expected to be more homogeneous than groups of eight are. The greater homogeneity means that smaller errors affect the comparisons. Significant results will be announced more frequently when they should be.

Confounding has many applications in more complex designs. For a discussion of such possibilities, see Bennett and Franklin,[1] Cochran and Cox,[2] Fisher,[3] and Kempthorne.[4] Although confounding is a potentially valuable method for the psychologist who wishes to reduce the magnitude of the errors in his research, the method has been applied infrequently. Unfortunately the use of the term "confounding" occurs most often in criticism of poor designs in which an unintended, and perhaps unfortunate, mixing-together of sources of variability occurs.

REFERENCES

1. Bennett, C.A., and Franklin, N.L., *Statistical Analysis in Chemistry and the Chemical Industry*. New York: John Wiley and Sons, Inc., 1954.
2. Cochran, W.G., and Cox, G.M., *Experimental Designs*. New York: John Wiley and Sons, Inc., 1950.
3. Fisher, R.A., *The Design of Experiments*. New York: Hafner Publishing Co., Inc., 1949.
4. Kempthorne, C.E., *The Design and Analysis of Experiments*. New York: John Wiley and Sons, Inc., 1952.

FACTORIAL DESIGNS
WITH ADJUSTING

13

The analysis of covariance can be incorporated in factorial designs, combining precision and comprehensiveness in psychological experiments. In general, the experimenter obtains a number of random samples of subjects. The number of samples is determined, in a factorial design, by the number of combinations of treatments. The experimenter chooses, as an adjusting variable, a response variable which is linearly correlated with the dependent variable. He measures all subjects in the several samples under uniform conditions on the adjusting variable. He then assigns the treatment combinations randomly to the samples. He imposes the treatments and obtains the final observations on the dependent variable. Using the regression of the dependent variable on the adjusting variable, he removes part of the variability in his observations associated with initial differences among his subjects. The remaining variability is analyzed and apparent treatment effects are evaluated by comparison with an estimate of the errors which might actually have produced them.

TWO FACTORS

The 2×2 design prescribes four treatment combinations, 1, a, b and ab, and, for a covariance analysis, requires four random samples of subjects. One treatment combination is assigned to a sample. Table 13.1 presents the arrangement of subjects, treatments, and observations on the adjusting variable, X, and the dependent variable, Y.

In the analysis of the data, two kinds of adjustments are performed. The one kind yields the error sum of squares and only has to be done once.

175

		A_1					A_2		
			1					a	
		1	X_1	Y_1			1	X_1	Y_1
		2	X_2	Y_2			2	X_2	Y_2
		.	.				.	.	
B_1	Ss	i	X_i	Y_i		Ss	i	X_i	Y_i
		.	.				.	.	
		n	X_n	Y_n			n	X_n	Y_n
			b					ab	
		1	X_1	Y_1			1	X_1	Y_1
		2	X_2	Y_2			2	X_2	Y_2
		.	.				.	.	
B_2	Ss	i	X_i	Y_i		Ss	i	X_i	Y_i
		.	.				.	.	
		n	X_n	Y_n			n	X_n	Y_n

The other kind of adjustment has to be done three times, once for each treatment effect. Each of the three results of this second type of adjustment can be used with the error sum of squares in the computation of the discrepancy sum of squares for a particular treatment effect. These three discrepancy components must then be evaluated in tests of significance.

Before these adjustments can be performed, a fairly extensive preliminary analysis of the data must be undertaken. The adjustments will be presented after a detailed description of the preliminary analysis.

The total sum of squares for Y, the dependent variable, can be analyzed into four components: A_y, B_y, AB_y, and the within-sample sum of squares, W_y. If we let 1_y, a_y, b_y, and ab_y be sample sums for the dependent variable, and C'_y be the correction term, then the three treatment components are

$$A_y = \frac{(a_y + ab_y)^2 + (1_y + b_y)^2}{2n} - C'_y,$$

$$B_y = \frac{(b_y + ab_y)^2 + (1_y + a_y)^2}{2n} - C'_y,$$

$$AB_y = \frac{(1_y + ab_y)^2 + (a_y + b_y)^2}{2n} - C'_y.$$

W_y is obtained by combining the four sample sums of squares, each of which can be computed by formula (4.1),

$$\Sigma Y^2 - \frac{(\Sigma Y)^2}{n},$$

where the summations have n terms.

In a similar fashion, the total sum of squares for X, the adjusting variable, can be divided into four parts. The three treatment components are

$$A_x = \frac{(a_x + ab_x)^2 + (1_x + b_x)^2}{2n} - C'_x,$$

$$B_x = \frac{(b_x + ab_x)^2 + (1_x + a_x)^2}{2n} - C'_x,$$

$$AB_x = \frac{(1_x + ab_x)^2 + (a_x + b_x)^2}{2n} - C'_x.$$

W_x is obtained by combining the four sample sums of squares, each of which can be computed by formula (4.1),

$$\Sigma X^2 - \frac{(\Sigma X)^2}{n},$$

where the summations have n terms.

An important new feature in the analysis is the subdivision of the total covariation or sum of products of deviations into four parts: three treatment components, A_{xy}, B_{xy}, and AB_{xy}, and the within-sample sum of products, W_{xy}.

Let us digress for a moment and consider the three components of covariation for the treatment effects. Eliminating the within-sample covariation from the total covariation provides the means of conceptualizing the between-sample covariation. This elimination can be accomplished by a very simple set of operations. The mean of X and the mean of Y are computed for each sample and substituted for each of the n values in that sample. Since all of the substituted values on either variable, within any sample, are the same, there can be no covariation within samples. Any remaining covariation can be described as the covariation of differences among the four samples on X and differences among the four samples on Y. This covariation among samples can be analyzed into three components, corresponding to A, B, and AB.

These components of covariation can be conceptualized in the following manner. Consider the covariation for A. The variability within each level of A can be eliminated, for X and for Y, by substituting the mean of each level for all observations at that level. The covariation within each level is thereby eliminated. The remaining covariation can be described as the covariation of differences between levels of A.

If the columns of our tabulation of data for the 2×2 design correspond to levels of A, then the covariation for A is a between-column sum of products of deviations which is defined specifically as follows. Let $\bar{X}_{.k}$ and $\bar{Y}_{.k}$ be means of the kth column. Let $\bar{X}_{..}$ and $\bar{Y}_{..}$ be total means. The product of deviations for the means of any column is

$$(\bar{X}_{.k} - \bar{X}_{..})(\bar{Y}_{.k} - \bar{Y}_{..}).$$

Since this product represents $2n$ values in the column, it is multiplied by $2n$, giving

$$2n(\bar{X}_{.k} - \bar{X}_{..})(\bar{Y}_{.k} - \bar{Y}_{..}).$$

Summing for both columns, we have

$$\Sigma 2n(\bar{X}_{.k} - \bar{X}_{..})(\bar{Y}_{.k} - \bar{Y}_{..}),$$

which is called the between-column sum of products or covariation. Similar expressions can be written for rows, representing levels of B, and for diagonals, representing the interaction comparison for AB. Computing formulas for components of covariation are similar, in certain respects, to formula (4.3) and, in other respects, to formula (10.1). The student will profit from a careful examination of formulas (4.3) and (10.1) and those given below.

If we let

$$C'_{xy} = \frac{(1_x + a_x + b_x + ab_x)(1_y + a_y + b_y + ab_y)}{N},$$

then

$$A_{xy} = \frac{(a_x + ab_x)(a_y + ab_y) + (1_x + b_x)(1_y + b_y)}{2n} - C'_{xy}.$$

(Compare the formula for A_{xy} with that for A_x and A_y.)

$$B_{xy} = \frac{(b_x + ab_x)(b_y + ab_y) + (1_x + a_x)(1_y + a_y)}{2n} - C'_{xy},$$

$$AB_{xy} = \frac{(1_x + ab_x)(1_y + ab_y) + (a_x + b_x)(a_y + b_y)}{2n} - C'_{xy}.$$

W_{xy} is obtained by combining the four sample sums of products, each of which can be computed by a formula adapted from formula (10.1),

$$\Sigma XY - \frac{(\Sigma X)(\Sigma Y)}{n},$$

where the summations have n terms.

The preliminary analysis is now complete. The adjustments will be described next.

For each treatment effect, two steps must be taken. First, subtotal sums of squares and products must be constituted. Second, the subtotal sum of squares for Y must be adjusted.

The subtotal sums of squares and products for A are defined as

$$(A_y + W_y),$$
$$(A_x + W_x),$$
$$(A_{xy} + W_{xy}).$$

The adjustment of the subtotal for A takes the characteristic form*

$$\Sigma y^2 - \frac{(\Sigma xy)^2}{\Sigma x^2},$$

which in the present notation becomes

$$(A_y + W_y) - \frac{(A_{xy} + W_{xy})}{A_x + W_x}.$$

The adjustment yields a subtotal sum of squares of errors of prediction which we shall designate

$$A_e.$$

The subtotal sums of squares and products for B are synthesized as follows:

$$(B_y + \widetilde{W_y}),$$
$$(B_x + W_x),$$
$$(B_{xy} + W_{xy}).$$

The adjustment of the subtotal for B is

$$B_e = (B_y + W_y) - \frac{(B_{xy} + W_{xy})^2}{B_x + W_x}.$$

---

* See the adjustment of the total sum of squares on page 113.

The subtotal sums of squares and products for AB are

$$(AB_y + W_y),$$
$$(AB_x + W_x),$$
$$(AB_{xy} + W_{xy}).$$

The adjustment for AB is

$$AB_e = (AB_y + W_y) - \frac{(AB_{xy} + W_{xy})}{AB_x + W_x}.$$

The adjustment of the within-sample sum of squares of Y yields W_e, the within-sample sum of squares of errors of prediction, a measure of error. The adjustment is

$$W_e = W_y - \frac{W_{xy}^2}{W_x}.$$

All the adjustments have now been completed. The next step is the computation of a discrepancy sum of squares for each of the treatment effects. D_a, the discrepancy sum of squares for the main effect A is

$$D_a = A_e - W_e.$$

The others are

$$D_b = B_e - W_e,$$

$$D_{ab} = AB_e - W_e.$$

Tests of significance can now be performed with treatment variances computed from the discrepancy sums of squares and an error variance computed from W_e, the within-sample sum of squares of errors of prediction. The form of the analysis is given in Table 13.2.

Table 13.2

**GENERAL FORM OF THE ANALYSIS OF COVARIANCE
FOR A 2×2 DESIGN**

Component	SS	df	V	F
A	D_a	1	V_a	V_a/V_e
B	D_b	1	V_b	V_b/V_e
AB	D_{ab}	1	V_{ab}	V_{ab}/V_e
Error	W_e	$N-5$	V_e	

$N = 4n = $ total number of subjects

It may be helpful to point out the parallel between the adjustment in the single-factor problem of Chapter 10 and the adjustments of the 2×2 design described above. In the single-variable situation, where only one treatment effect has to be evaluated, the total sum of squares of Y is adjusted and the sum of squares of errors of prediction that results is employed in computing a discrepancy sum of squares. The analysis of the 2×2 design can be thought of as consisting of three such operations. One sets up three problems, one for each of the treatment effects. A subtotal sum of squares is manufactured which contains, in each instance, only one treatment effect because the others have been left out. Thus the adjustment of each subtotal in a factorial design parallels the one adjustment of the total in the single-factor problem.

THREE FACTORS

In the $2 \times 2 \times 2$ covariance design, eight treatment combinations are defined and, consequently, eight samples of subjects are needed. Table 13.3 shows the appropriate arrangement of samples and treatments. Each cell of a 2×2 table is a sample of n subjects. Subjects are measured on the

Table 13.3

THE ARRANGEMENT OF SAMPLES IN THE $2 \times 2 \times 2$ COVARIANCE DESIGN WITH TREATMENT COMBINATIONS AND SAMPLE SUMS INDICATED

	C_1				C_2		
	A_1		A_2		A_1		A_2
B_1	1_x 1_y		a_x a_y	B_1	c_x c_y		ac_x ac_y
B_2	b_x b_y		ab_x ab_y	B_2	bc_x bc_y		abc_x abc_y

adjusting variable, X, before the experiment. Measures on the dependent variable, Y, are then obtained. The symbols in each cell show the treatment for that sample but also will be taken to represent the two sample sums, one for X and one for Y.

The preliminary analysis involves computing sums of squares and products for the seven treatment effects and the within-sample variability. The writing of the formulas for these components of variation and covariation will be facilitated by letting

$$A_{1Y} = 1_y + b_y + c_y + bc_y,$$
$$A_{2Y} = a_y + ab_y + ac_y + abc_y,$$
$$B_{1Y} = 1_y + a_y + c_y + ac_y,$$
$$B_{2Y} = b_y + ab_y + bc_y + abc_y,$$
$$C_{1Y} = 1_y + a_y + b_y + ab_y,$$
$$C_{2Y} = c_y + ac_y + bc_y + abc_y,$$
$$AB_{1Y} = 1_y + c_y + ab_y + abc_y,$$
$$AB_{2Y} = a_y + b_y + ac_y + bc_y,$$
$$AC_{1Y} = 1_y + b_y + ac_y + abc_y,$$
$$AC_{2Y} = a_y + c_y + ab_y + bc_y,$$
$$BC_{1Y} = 1_y + a_y + bc_y + abc_y,$$
$$BC_{2Y} = b_y + c_y + ab_y + ac_y,$$
$$ABC_{1Y} = 1_y + ab_y + ac_y + bc_y,$$
$$ABC_{2Y} = a_y + b_y + c_y + abc_y.$$

Then the seven components of variability in Y are

$$A_y = \frac{A_{1Y}^2 + A_{2Y}^2}{4n} - C_y',$$

$$B_y = \frac{B_{1Y}^2 + B_{2Y}^2}{4n} - C_y',$$

$$C_y = \frac{C_{1Y}^2 + C_{2Y}^2}{4n} - C_y',$$

$$AB_y = \frac{AB_{1Y}^2 + AB_{2Y}^2}{4n} - C_y',$$

$$AC_y = \frac{AC_{1Y}^2 + AC_{2Y}^2}{4n} - C_y',$$

$$BC_y = \frac{BC_{1Y}^2 + BC_{2Y}^2}{4n} - C_y',$$

$$ABC_y = \frac{ABC_{1Y}^2 + ABC_{2Y}^2}{4n} - C_y'.$$

W_y is obtained by combining the eight sample sums of squares, each of which can be computed by formula (4.1):

$$\Sigma Y^2 - \frac{(\Sigma Y)^2}{n},$$

where there are n terms in the summations.

By changing all the subscript letters from Y to X in the formulas, we obtain the corresponding components of variability for the adjusting measures as follows:

$$A_x = \frac{A_{1X}^2 + A_{2X}^2}{4n} - C_x',$$

$$B_x = \frac{B_{1X}^2 + B_{2X}^2}{4n} - C_x',$$

$$C_x = \frac{C_{1X}^2 + C_{2X}^2}{4n} - C_x',$$

$$AB_x = \frac{AB_{1X}^2 + AB_{2X}^2}{4n} - C_x',$$

$$AC_x = \frac{AC_{1X}^2 + AC_{2X}^2}{4n} - C_x',$$

$$BC_x = \frac{BC_{1X}^2 + BC_{2X}^2}{4n} - C_x',$$

$$ABC_x = \frac{ABC_{1X}^2 + ABC_{2X}^2}{4n} - C_x'.$$

W_x is obtained by combining the eight sample sums of squares, each of which is computed by the formula

$$\Sigma X^2 - \frac{(\Sigma X)^2}{n},$$

where there are n terms in the summations.

The covariation can be analyzed in a similar fashion. We let

$$C_{xy}' = \frac{(\Sigma X)(\Sigma Y)}{N},$$

where the summations have $N = 8n$ terms. Then, to obtain A_{xy}, the sum of products for A, the sums A_{1x} and A_{2x} for the adjusting variable, and the sums A_{1Y} and A_{2Y} for the dependent variable can be substituted in

$$A_{xy} = \frac{A_{1X}A_{1Y} + A_{2X}A_{2Y}}{4n} - C_{xy}'.$$

By substituting the appropriate sums in the following formulas, we can obtain the other six components of covariation:

$$B_{xy} = \frac{B_{1X}B_{1Y} + B_{2X}B_{2Y}}{4n} - C'_{xy},$$

$$C_{xy} = \frac{C_{1X}C_{1Y} + C_{2X}C_{2Y}}{4n} - C'_{xy},$$

$$AB_{xy} = \frac{AB_{1X}AB_{1Y} + AB_{2X}AB_{2Y}}{4n} - C'_{xy},$$

$$AC_{xy} = \frac{AC_{1X}AC_{1Y} + AC_{2X}AC_{2Y}}{4n} - C'_{xy},$$

$$BC_{xy} = \frac{BC_{1X}BC_{1Y} + BC_{2X}BC_{2Y}}{4n} - C'_{xy},$$

$$ABC_{xy} = \frac{ABC_{1X}ABC_{1Y} + ABC_{2X}ABC_{2Y}}{4n} - C'_{xy}.$$

W_{xy}, the combined within-sample sum of products, is obtained by combining the sums of products for the eight samples. Each sample sum of products is computed by a modification of formula (10.1):

$$\Sigma XY - \frac{(\Sigma X)(\Sigma Y)}{n},$$

where there are n terms in each summation.

Subtotal sums of squares and products are next constituted for the seven treatment effects as indicated in Table 13.4. These sums of squares and products are used in effecting the seven adjustments listed below. Each adjustment yields a sum of squares of errors of prediction:

$$A_e = (A_y + W_y) \quad - \quad \frac{(A_{xy} + W_{xy})^2}{A_x + W_x},$$

$$B_e = (B_y + W_y) \quad - \quad \frac{(B_{xy} + W_{xy})^2}{B_x + W_x},$$

$$C_e = (C_y + W_y) \quad - \quad \frac{(C_{xy} + W_{xy})^2}{C_x + W_x},$$

$$AB_e = (AB_y + W_y) \quad - \quad \frac{(AB_{xy} + W_{xy})^2}{AB_x + W_x},$$

$$AC_e = (AC_y + W_y) \quad - \quad \frac{(AC_{xy} + W_{xy})^2}{AC_x + W_x},$$

$$BC_e = (BC_y + W_y) \quad - \quad \frac{(BC_{xy} + W_{xy})^2}{BC_x + W_x},$$

$$ABC_e = (ABC_y + W_y) - \frac{(ABC_{xy} + W_{xy})^2}{ABC_x + W_x}.$$

The adjustment of the within-sample variability is given by

$$W_e = W_y - \frac{W_{xy}^2}{W_x}.$$

Table 13.4
SUBTOTAL SUMS OF SQUARES AND PRODUCTS FOR THE $2 \times 2 \times 2$ COVARIANCE DESIGN

Treatment	Dependent variation	Covariation	Adjusting Variation
A	$A_y + W_y$	$A_{xy} + W_{xy}$	$A_x + W_x$
B	$B_y + W_y$	$B_{xy} + W_{xy}$	$B_x + W_x$
C	$C_y + W_y$	$C_{xy} + W_{xy}$	$C_x + W_x$
AB	$AB_y + W_y$	$AB_{xy} + W_{xy}$	$AB_x + W_x$
AC	$AC_y + W_y$	$AC_{xy} + W_{xy}$	$AC_x + W_x$
BC	$BC_y + W_y$	$BC_{xy} + W_{xy}$	$BC_x + W_x$
ABC	$ABC_y + W_y$	$ABC_{xy} + W_{xy}$	$ABC_x + W_x$

D_a, the discrepancy sum of squares for A and a measure of the apparent treatment effect for A, is computed by

$$D_a = A_e - W_e.$$

The other six discrepancy sums of squares are

$$D_b = B_e - W_e,$$
$$D_c = C_e - W_e,$$
$$D_{ab} = AB_e - W_e,$$
$$D_{ac} = AC_e - W_e,$$
$$D_{bc} = BC_e - W_e,$$
$$D_{abc} = ABC_e - W_e.$$

Treatment variances can now be computed from the discrepancy sums of squares and an error variance from W_e, the within-sample sum of squares of errors of estimate. Tests of significance are then performed. The form of the analysis is given in Table 13.5.

AN EXAMPLE

A psychologist did an experiment to determine the effect of noise, practice, and medium of communication on the performances of male, ROTC students on an oral directions test. Two levels of intensity of white noise (A) were employed. Two amounts of practice (B) were permitted. Two systems (C) of administering the test were employed: a conventional public address system and a closed-circuit television system. Subjects were tested initially on a

Table 13.5
GENERAL FORM OF THE ANALYSIS OF COVARIANCE
FOR A $2 \times 2 \times 2$ DESIGN

Component	SS	df	V	F
A	D_a	1	V_a	V_a/V_e
B	D_b	1	V_b	V_b/V_e
C	D_c	1	V_c	V_c/V_e
AB	D_{ab}	1	V_{ab}	V_{ab}/V_e
AC	D_{ac}	1	V_{ac}	V_{ac}/V_e
BC	D_{bc}	1	V_{bc}	V_{bc}/V_e
ABC	D_{abc}	1	V_{abc}	V_{abc}/V_e
Error	W_e	$8n - 9$	V_e	

n = number of subjects in each sample
$N = 8n$ = total number of subjects

paper-and-pencil directions test.   Scores on the initial test and the final test
are given in Table 13.6.

Table 13.6
DATA FOR THE ORAL DIRECTIONS EXPERIMENT

		C_1				C_2		
	\multicolumn{2}{c}{A_1}	\multicolumn{2}{c}{A_2}		\multicolumn{2}{c}{A_1}	\multicolumn{2}{c}{A_2}

	\multicolumn{2}{c}{1}	\multicolumn{2}{c}{a}		\multicolumn{2}{c}{c}	\multicolumn{2}{c}{ac}
	X	Y	X	Y		X	Y	X	Y
B_1	22	20	21	23	B_1	21	21	22	24
	24	23	27	30		25	24	23	25
	26	26	26	29		28	28	26	29
	26	27	22	26		26	27	28	32
	19	21	21	24		22	22	23	27

	\multicolumn{2}{c}{b}	\multicolumn{2}{c}{ab}		\multicolumn{2}{c}{bc}	\multicolumn{2}{c}{abc}
	X	Y	X	Y		X	Y	X	Y
B_2	22	21	18	22		23	23	25	29
	26	26	22	26		22	22	21	26
	23	24	25	30		24	25	18	24
	25	27	23	29		27	29	18	25
	26	29	21	27		26	28	14	22

A: noise levels
B: practice levels
C: communication media
X: directions pretest; Y: oral directions test

The first step in the preliminary analysis involves combining the appropriate sample sums to obtain

$$A_{1Y} = 493, \qquad A_{2Y} = 529,$$
$$B_{1Y} = 508, \qquad B_{2Y} = 514,$$
$$C_{1Y} = 510, \qquad C_{2Y} = 512,$$
$$AB_{1Y} = 499, \qquad AB_{2Y} = 523,$$
$$AC_{1Y} = 507, \qquad AC_{2Y} = 515,$$
$$BC_{1Y} = 502, \qquad BC_{2Y} = 520,$$
$$ABC_{1Y} = 515, \qquad ABC_{2Y} = 507,$$

and also

$$A_{1X} = 483, \qquad A_{2X} = 444,$$
$$B_{1X} = 478, \qquad B_{2X} = 449,$$
$$C_{1X} = 465, \qquad C_{2X} = 462,$$
$$AB_{1X} = 444, \qquad AB_{2X} = 483,$$
$$AC_{1X} = 457, \qquad AC_{2X} = 470,$$
$$BC_{1X} = 452, \qquad BC_{2X} = 475,$$
$$ABC_{1X} = 470, \qquad ABC_{2X} = 457.$$

The sums given above are substituted below in appropriate formulas to provide the seven components of variability in Y for the seven treatment effects. Note that $C'_y = (1022)^2/40$.

$$A_y = (493^2 + 529^2)/20 - (1022)^2/40 = 32.40,$$
$$B_y = (508^2 + 514^2)/20 - (1022)^2/40 = 0.90,$$
$$C_y = (510^2 + 512^2)/20 - (1022)^2/40 = 0.10,$$
$$AB_y = (499^2 + 523^2)/20 - (1022)^2/40 = 14.40,$$
$$AC_y = (507^2 + 515^2)/20 - (1022)^2/40 = 1.60,$$
$$BC_y = (502^2 + 520^2)/20 - (1022)^2/40 = 8.10,$$
$$ABC_y = (515^2 + 507^2)/20 - (1022)^2/40 = 1.60.$$

Note that $C'_x = (927)^2/40$. The seven components of variability in X are

$$A_x = (483^2 + 444^2)/20 - (927)^2/40 = 38.02,$$
$$B_x = (478^2 + 449^2)/20 - (927)^2/40 = 21.02,$$
$$C_x = (465^2 + 462^2)/20 - (927)^2/40 = 0.22,$$
$$AB_x = (444^2 + 483^2)/20 - (927)^2/40 = 38.02,$$
$$AC_x = (457^2 + 470^2)/20 - (927)^2/40 = 4.22,$$
$$BC_x = (452^2 + 475^2)/20 - (927)^2/40 = 13.22,$$
$$ABC_x = (470^2 + 457^2)/20 - (927)^2/40 = 4.22.$$

Note that $C'_{xy} = (927)(1022)/40$. Components of covariation for the seven treatment effects are

$$A_{xy} = (483 \times 493 + 444 \times 529)/20 - (927)(1022)/40 = -35.10,$$
$$B_{xy} = (478 \times 508 + 449 \times 514)/20 - (927)(1022)/40 = -\ 4.35,$$
$$C_{xy} = (465 \times 510 + 462 \times 512)/20 - (927)(1022)/40 = -\ 0.15,$$
$$AB_{xy} = (444 \times 499 + 483 \times 523)/20 - (927)(1022)/40 = \ 23.40,$$
$$AC_{xy} = (457 \times 507 + 470 \times 515)/20 - (927)(1022)/40 = \ \ 2.60,$$
$$BC_{xy} = (452 \times 502 + 475 \times 520)/20 - (927)(1022)/40 = \ 10.35,$$
$$ABC_{xy} = (470 \times 515 + 457 \times 507)/20 - (927)(1022)/40 = \ \ 2.60.$$

The combined within-sample sums of squares and products are

$$W_y = 292.8,$$
$$W_x = 250.8,$$
$$W_{xy} = 248.8.$$

The individual sample sums of squares and products are given in Table 13.7.

Table 13.7
SAMPLE SUMS OF SQUARES AND PRODUCTS
FOR THE $2 \times 2 \times 2$ COVARIANCE EXAMPLE*

	Σy^2	Σxy	Σx^2
1	37.2	31.2	35.2
a	37.2	34.2	33.2
b	37.2	20.2	13.2
c	37.2	34.2	33.2
ab	38.8	30.8	26.8
ac	41.2	31.2	25.2
bc	37.2	25.2	17.2
abc	26.8	41.8	66.8
	$W_y = 292.8$	$W_{xy} = 248.8$	$W_x = 250.8$

* Data in Table 13.6

If one computes the total sums of squares and products, there is a valuable check on accuracy of computation which can be applied at this point. The total sum of squares for Y is 351.90. It should equal the sum of the seven treatment components, which is 59.1, plus the within-sample sum of squares, which is 292.8. That is,

$$351.9 = \ 59.1 \ + 292.8.$$

The check on the computation for X is

$$369.78 = 118.98 + 250.80.$$

The check on the computation of the covariation is

$$248.15 = -0.65 + 248.80.$$

The next step is the synthesis of the subtotal sums of squares and products for the seven treatment effects.   Table 13.8 shows the quantities used and the results of the syntheses.

Table 13.8

SUBTOTAL SUMS OF SQUARES AND PRODUCTS FOR THE $2 \times 2 \times 2$ COVARIANCE EXAMPLE*

	$A_y + W_y =$	$32.40 + 292.80 = 325.20$
A	$A_{xy} + W_{xy} =$	$-35.10 + 248.80 = 213.70$
	$A_x + W_x =$	$38.02 + 250.80 = 288.82$
	$B_y + W_y =$	$0.90 + 292.80 = 293.70$
B	$B_{xy} + W_{xy} =$	$-4.35 + 248.80 = 244.45$
	$B_x + W_x =$	$21.02 + 250.80 = 271.82$
	$C_y + W_y =$	$0.10 + 292.80 = 292.90$
C	$C_{xy} + W_{xy} =$	$-0.15 + 248.80 = 248.65$
	$C_x + W_x =$	$0.22 + 250.80 = 251.02$
	$AB_y + W_y =$	$14.40 + 292.80 = 307.20$
AB	$AB_{xy} + W_{xy} =$	$23.40 + 248.80 = 272.20$
	$AB_x + W_x =$	$38.02 + 250.80 = 288.82$
	$AC_y + W_y =$	$1.60 + 292.80 = 294.40$
AC	$AC_{xy} + W_{xy} =$	$2.60 + 248.80 = 251.40$
	$AC_x + W_x =$	$4.22 + 250.80 = 255.02$
	$BC_y + W_y =$	$8.10 + 292.80 = 300.90$
BC	$BC_{xy} + W_{xy} =$	$10.35 + 248.80 = 259.15$
	$BC_x + W_x =$	$13.22 + 250.80 = 264.02$
	$ABC_y + W_y =$	$1.60 + 292.80 = 294.40$
ABC	$ABC_{xy} + W_{xy} =$	$2.60 + 248.80 = 251.40$
	$ABC_x + W_x =$	$4.22 + 250.80 = 255.02$

* Data in Table 13.6

The subtotal sums of squares and products are then employed in the adjustments, which yield sums of squares of errors of prediction for the seven treatment effects, as follows:

$$A_e = 325.20 - (213.70)^2/288.82 = 167.08,$$
$$B_e = 293.70 - (244.45)^2/271.82 = 73.86,$$
$$C_e = 292.90 - (248.65)^2/251.02 = 46.60,$$
$$AB_e = 307.20 - (272.20)^2/288.82 = 50.66,$$
$$AC_e = 294.40 - (251.40)^2/255.02 = 46.57,$$
$$BC_e = 300.90 - (259.15)^2/264.02 = 46.53,$$
$$ABC_e = 294.40 - (251.40)^2/255.02 = 46.57.$$

The adjustment of the within-sample variability that yields W_e, the measure of error, is

$$W_e = 292.80 - (248.80)^2/250.80 = 45.98.$$

D_a, the discrepancy sum of squares for A, is obtained as shown below:

$$D_a = A_e - W_e = 167.08 - 45.98 = 121.10.$$

The other six discrepancy sums of squares are obtained by similar computation. They are given in Table 13.9 with the corresponding variances and the appropriate F ratios for the seven tests of significance. Only the two main effects, level of noise and practice are significant.

Table 13.9

ANALYSIS OF COVARIANCE FOR THE EXPERIMENT ON ORAL DIRECTIONS*

Component	SS	df	V	F
Noise (A)	121.10	1	121.10	81.82†
Practice (B)	27.88	1	27.88	18.84†
Medium (C)	0.62	1	0.62	0.42
Noise × Practice (AB)	4.68	1	4.68	3.16
Noise × Medium (AC)	0.59	1	0.59	0.40
Medium × Practice (BC)	0.55	1	0.55	0.37
Noise × Practice × Medium (ABC)	0.59	1	0.59	0.40
Error	45.98	31	1.48	

* Data in Table 13.6
† Null hypothesis rejected
F_c, the criterion value for the 0.05 level of significance for 1 and 31 df is 4.16

The main analysis for the $2 \times 2 \times 2$, covariance example has now been completed. In actual practice, the experimenter would also test the significance of the regression, the homogeneity of the sample variances, and the homogeneity of the sample regressions. All of the information needed for these tests is contained in Table 13.7. It is left as an exercise for the student to carry them out.

To adjust the means of the levels of any treatment, one follows the procedure given in Chapter 10 for the single-factor problem. In a factorial design, however, the regression coefficient is computed from the subtotal sums of squares and products for the particular treatment in question.

COMPUTING INTERACTIONS

In rectangular designs in which the number of levels varies from one factor to another, it is most convenient to compute the interaction sums of squares and products by subtraction. For example, in a 2×3 design, the sums of squares of Y for differences between rows and between columns can be subtracted from the sum of squares for differences among the six samples, leaving as a remainder the interaction sum of squares for the dependent variable. The sum of squares of X for differences between rows and the sum of squares for differences between columns can be subtracted from the between-sample sum of squares for the adjusting variable, too. In similar fashion, the between-row sum of products and the between-column sum of products can be subtracted from the between-sample covariation, yielding the interaction covariation.

An alternative method of computation, which is less convenient than the subtraction method, has the advantage that it permits a check of the correctness of one's calculations. The method involves the computation of an interaction deviation for each sample mean on variable Y and a similar quantity for each sample on variable X. In the 2×3 design, an interaction deviation for Y, in the jth row and the kth column, is defined by formula (11.1) as

$$\bar{Y}_{jk} - \bar{Y}_{j.} - \bar{Y}_{.k} + \bar{Y}_{...}$$

Such a value can be computed for each of the six samples. These deviations are squared and, since each one must represent all of the values in that sample, are multiplied by n, as indicated below:

$$n(\bar{Y}_{jk} - \bar{Y}_{j.} - \bar{Y}_{.k} + \bar{Y}_{..})^2.$$

The six weighted squares are then summed, yielding the interaction sum of squares for Y. The same procedure can be employed with the adjusting variable. An interaction deviation for X is

$$\bar{X}_{jk} - \bar{X}_{j.} - \bar{X}_{.k} + \bar{X}_{..}$$

It is squared and weighted for the number of subjects in a sample. These weighted squares are then summed over the six samples.

The interaction covariation is obtained in much the same way. For each sample, a product

$$(\bar{X}_{jk} - \bar{X}_{j.} - \bar{X}_{.k} + \bar{X}_{..})(\bar{Y}_{jk} - \bar{Y}_{j.} - \bar{Y}_{.k} + \bar{Y}_{..})$$

is computed and multiplied by n. The six weighted products are summed, yielding the interaction sum of products.

The computational check is applied to the sums of squares and products separately, of course. That is, the total sum of squares for the dependent variable should equal the sum of the components for differences between rows, differences between columns, interaction, and differences within samples. The same check is then applied to the adjusting variable, and finally to the covariation.

Degrees of freedom for the general two-factor analysis of covariance are shown in Table 13.10. Those for the general three-factor covariance design are presented in Table 13.11.

Table 13.10

COMPONENTS OF VARIABILITY AND DEGREES OF FREEDOM FOR THE TWO-FACTOR COVARIANCE ANALYSIS

Component	df
A	$n_a - 1$
B	$n_b - 1$
AB	$(n_a - 1)(n_b - 1)$
Error	$n_a n_b (n - 1) - 1$

n_a = number of levels of A
n_b = number of levels of B
n = number of subjects per sample
$N = n_a n_b n$ = total number of subjects

Table 13.11

COMPONENTS OF VARIABILITY AND DEGREES OF FREEDOM
FOR THE THREE-FACTOR COVARIANCE ANALYSIS

Component	df
A	$n_a - 1$
B	$n_b - 1$
C	$n_c - 1$
AB	$(n_a - 1)(n_b - 1)$
AC	$(n_a - 1)(n_c - 1)$
BC	$(n_b - 1)(n_c - 1)$
ABC	$(n_a - 1)(n_b - 1)(n_c - 1)$
Error	$n_a n_b n_c (n - 1) - 1$

n_a = number of levels of A
n_b = number of levels of B
n_c = number of levels of C
n = number of subjects per sample
$N = n_a n_b n_c n$ = total number of subjects

SPECIFIC COMPARISONS

14

When a relatively complete and exact specification of the relation between a dependent variable and one or more independent variables is required and is possible, one tries to find an equation for a mathematical function which will adequately express the relation. On the one hand, the function may have an empirical origin, in which case the experimenter examines his data and then chooses the particular curve which appears to be appropriate. By one of several available methods of curve fitting, he determines the values of the constants in the equation. On the other hand, the function may have a rational origin, in which case the experimenter deduces from a body of theory the expected nature of the function. He may then test the goodness of fit of the theoretical curve to his experimental data.

In the early stages of research on problems in the behavioral sciences, it is seldom possible to use a mathematical function, whether empirical or theoretical in its origin, to specify the relation between the dependent variable in an experiment and one or more independent variables. As a matter of fact, the behavioral scientist, in the initial phases of research on a given problem, is often gratified to be able to announce that a difference on the dependent variable is related to a difference on the independent variable, even though he cannot state in what manner the difference varies throughout the possible range of treatment. His satisfaction in announcing merely a significant result, where the result is a difference or a set of differences, is further evidence of the partial nature of his knowledge. Being able to specify a mathematical function that relates a dependent variable and an independent variable, even when the function is only a crude approximation, represents a considerable acquisition of knowledge about a given phenomenon.

A reasonably ambitious step for the psychologist, in this connection, is the fitting of regression lines, linear and curvilinear, to experimental data. When there are more than two levels of treatment in a single-factor experiment and when these levels are themselves equally spaced on whatever scale is used to denote them, then the regression of the dependent variable on levels of the independent variable can be determined quite easily. The method, a special case of orthogonal polynomials, can be thought of as fitting a regression equation using the successive powers of the levels, or to be more exact, certain functions of the successive powers. With three levels of treatment, one can obtain the best-fitting straight line and also evaluate departures from linearity. With four levels, one can obtain the best-fitting parabola and also evaluate departures from that curve. The methods can be extended readily to larger numbers of levels.

The fitting of these various regression lines makes it possible to subdivide the over-all treatment differences for three or more levels into components of variability that are independent and which can be tested individually for significance. When there are three levels, a linear component and a component usually referred to as the *quadratic* component can be computed. The linear component is that part of the variability which is predictable from a linear regression equation. The quadratic component is the part not predictable. In the case of four levels, treatment variability can be subdivided into three components: linear, quadratic, and cubic. The linear component is variability predictable from the fitting of a straight line to the data. The quadratic component is variability predictable from fitting a parabola to the deviations from linearity. The cubic component is variability not predictable from the parabolic regression line or deviations from the parabolic trend.

The subdivision of an apparent treatment effect into two or more components is equivalent to the making of experimental comparisons more specific than those implicit in the over-all F test applied to three or more group means. There is an advantage in this specificity: real effects are more likely to be detected. For example, when there is a real linear effect and departures from linearity are due only to error, then the null hypothesis will be correctly rejected more often by the specific test of the linear component than by the over-all test.

INTERPRETATION OF TWO LEVELS

In the simplest one-factor experiment, which involves only two levels of treatment, little can be said about the function. Nothing can be said with confidence about the function for levels below and above those employed in the experiment. The direction of the difference on the dependent variable can, of course, be noted, but one cannot conclude that the direction would be constant if intermediate levels of the independent variable were used.   In

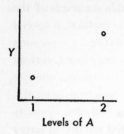

Fig. 14.1, the positions of two sample means, $\bar{Y}_{.1}$ and $\bar{Y}_{.2}$, have been plotted with reference to two axes. The abscissa is the scale of levels of treatment.   The ordinate is the scale of response on the dependent variable.   Caution must be exercised in the interpretation of the direction of the difference, with respect to its implications for the function relating the two variables, because observations at other intermediate levels could produce a variety of results which cannot be predicted from the evidence available on two levels. Examine Fig. 14.1 and consider the results which might conceivably be obtained if a third, intermediate level were added to the conditions.   Three possible outcomes are shown in Fig. 14.2.

Fig. 14.1 The plot of the means of two samples for a one-factor experiment where the two levels of treatment A are 1 and 2.

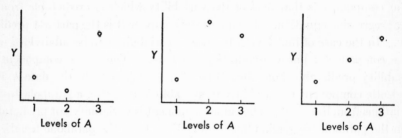

Fig. 14.2   Plots of three means for each of three different one-factor experiments with three levels of treatment A.

THREE LEVELS

When three levels of treatment are used, somewhat greater confidence in one's inference as to the characteristics of the true function is justified.   When the three points obtained from plotting three means, $\bar{Y}_{.1}$, $\bar{Y}_{.2}$, and $\bar{Y}_{.3}$, lie in a straight line as in the left half of Fig. 14.3, there is a strong suggestion that the function is linear, at least to a first approximation, although it is certainly possible that it is curved, as it is in the right half of Fig. 14.3, or that it takes any one of a great variety of other forms which would fit the three points.

With three levels of treatment, the over-all treatment effect is associated with two degrees of freedom representing two independent comparisons that can be made among the three levels.   It is possible to formulate the two independent comparisons so that one represents the linear trend and the other represents departures from linearity. Computation is so much easier when levels of treatment are equally spaced that we shall consider only that case.

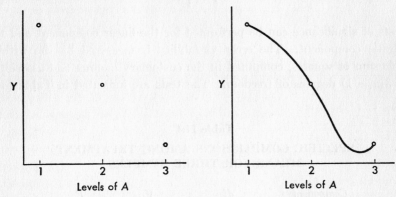

Fig. 14.3 In the left plot are the three sample means for the three treatment levels of a single factor. In the right plot there is drawn one possibility for the true function.

Let us examine the comparisons which can be made among three equally spaced levels of treatment, A_1, A_2, and A_3. Each treatment would be imposed on a sample of n subjects. If we let A_1, A_2, and A_3 also serve as the sums of samples at those levels, then the comparison for the linear trend is

$$A_3 - A_1.$$

A sum of squares for the linear trend can be computed by the formula

$$L = \frac{(A_3 - A_1)^2}{2n}.$$

Since one degree of freedom is associated with this linear component, the variance predicted by the linear regression equation is

$$V_L = \frac{L}{1}.$$

The comparison for departure from linearity is

$$2A_2 - A_1 - A_3.$$

A sum of squares for departures from linearity, that is, the quadratic component, is computed by

$$Q = \frac{(2A_2 - A_1 - A_3)^2}{6n}.$$

One degree of freedom is associated with the quadratic component. Therefore the variance of departures from linearity is

$$V_Q = \frac{Q}{1}.$$

Tests of significance can be performed for the linear component and the quadratic component. The error variability is measured by the within-sample sum of squares, computed in the customary manner and associated with $3(n-1)$ degrees of freedom. The tests are indicated in Table 14.1.

Table 14.1

SPECIFIC COMPARISONS AMONG TREATMENT MEANS FOR THREE SAMPLES

Component	df	V	F
Levels of A	2		
L	1	V_L	V_L/V_e
Q	1	V_Q	V_Q/V_e
Error	$3(n-1)$	V_e	
Total	$N-1$		

n = number of subjects per sample
$N = 3n$ = total number of subjects

AN EXAMPLE WITH MATCHING

Treatment effects in the matched group data of Table 9.7 can be analyzed into linear and quadratic components. The earlier analysis yielded the components and results in Table 9.9. Note that treatment effects in the earlier analysis were not significant, and that the treatment levels are equally spaced.

The same error variance can be used in the present analysis. The residual sum of squares was 712 with 14 degrees of freedom, giving a residual variance of 50.86. In the new analysis, all that we need to do, in addition to what was done in the analysis of Chapter 9, is to subdivide the sum of squares for levels of reward into linear and quadratic components. The sum of squares for levels of reward was 336.

The sums of the three levels are

$$A_1 = 200,$$
$$A_2 = 248,$$
$$A_3 = 272.$$

The linear component is

$$L = \frac{(A_3 - A_1)^2}{2r},$$

where r is the number of matched groups. In the example, $r = 8$. Substituting gives

$$L = (272 - 200)^2/2(8) = 324.$$

The quadratic component is

$$Q = \frac{(2A_2 - A_1 - A_3)^2}{6r}.$$

Substituting yields

$$Q = (2 \times 248 - 200 - 272)^2/6(8) = 12.$$

The results check in that the original sum of squares for levels equals the sum of the linear and quadratic components. That is,

$$336 = 324 + 12.$$

The complete analysis is given in Table 14.2. The linear trend is significant. Departures from linearity are not significant. In the earlier test of significance of the over-all differences, the null hypothesis was accepted. In

Table 14.2

SPECIFIC COMPARISONS IN THE DART THROWING DATA FOR THE MATCHED GROUP DESIGN*

Component	SS	df	V	F
Levels of reward	336	2		
L	324	1	324	6.37†
Q	12	1	12	0.24
Error	712	14	50.86	
Groups	384	7		
Total	1432	23		

* Data in Table 9.7; original analysis in Table 9.9
† Null hypothesis rejected; $F_c = 4.60$ for 1 and 14 df

Fig. 14.4 the means and the best-fitting linear regression line have been plotted.

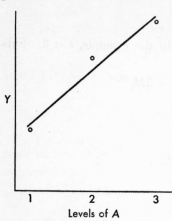

Fig. 14.4 Plot of the means and the best-fitting linear regression line for the matched-group data given in Table 9.7.

Levels of A

The slope of the regression line in Fig. 14.4 is 4.5. It was computed as follows. The formula for a regression coefficient, in general, is

$$b = \frac{\Sigma xy}{\Sigma x^2},$$

where y is the predicted variable and x is the predictor variable. Here we are concerned with the three means, $\bar{Y}_{.1} = 25$, $\bar{Y}_{.2} = 31$, and $\bar{Y}_{.3} = 34$, the corresponding levels of A that have the values* 1, 2, and 3, and the prediction of the means from the levels. Transformed to deviations, the means become -5, $+1$, and $+4$; the levels of A become -1, 0, and $+1$. The numerator of the regression coefficient will be the sum of products of these two sets of deviations; that is,

$$(-1)(-5) + (0)(1) + (1)(4) = 9.$$

The denominator is the sum of squares for levels of A; that is,

$$(-1)^2 + (0)^2 + (1)^2 = 2.$$

The regression coefficient, which is the slope of the line in Fig. 14.4, is the ratio

$$b = \frac{9}{2} = 4.5.$$

The linear prediction equation in deviation form is, in general,

$$y' = bx.$$

The predicted values as deviations from $\bar{Y}_{..} = 30$ are

$$(4.5)(-1) = -4.5,$$
$$(4.5)(0) = 0,$$
$$(4.5)(1) = 4.5.$$

---

* Note that three equally spaced levels can always be coded to values of 1, 2, and 3 without affecting the prediction.

The predicted values of Y are therefore

$$30 - 4.5 = 25.5,$$
$$30 + 0 \quad = 30,$$
$$30 + 4.5 = 34.5.$$

These are the values through which the regression line of Fig. 14.4 was drawn.

AN EXAMPLE WITH ADJUSTING

Table 14.3 gives data for three equally spaced levels of treatment imposed on three samples of subjects with measurement, before the experiment, on the adjusting variable, X, and after treatment, on the dependent variable, Y.

Table 14.3
DATA FOR THREE LEVELS OF A SINGLE-FACTOR COVARIANCE DESIGN

Levels of A

A_1		A_2		A_3	
X	Y	X	Y	X	Y
1	1	2	3	1	2
2	2	2	3	2	1
1	2	2	4	3	3
3	3	1	2	2	2
2	1	1	2	2	2

Note: The three levels are equally spaced.

The preliminary analysis involves the computation of linear and quadratic components of the sums of squares and products, as follows:

$$L_y = \frac{(A_{3Y} - A_{1Y})^2}{2n}$$

$$= (10 - 9)^2/10 = 0.10,$$

$$L_x = \frac{(A_{3X} - A_{1X})^2}{2n}$$

$$= (10 - 9)^2/10 = 0.10,$$

$$L_{xy} = \frac{(A_{3X} - A_{1X})(A_{3Y} - A_{1Y})}{2n}$$

$$= (10 - 9)(10 - 9)/10 = 0.10,$$

$$Q_y = \frac{(2A_{2Y} - A_{1Y} - A_{3Y})^2}{6n}$$

$$= (28 - 9 - 10)^2/30 = 2.70,$$

$$Q_x = \frac{(2A_{2X} - A_{1X} - A_{3X})^2}{6n}$$

$$= (16 - 9 - 10)^2/30 = 0.30,$$

$$Q_{xy} = \frac{(2A_{2X} - A_{1X} - A_{3X})(2A_{2Y} - A_{1Y} - A_{3Y})}{6n}$$

$$= (16 - 9 - 10)(28 - 9 - 10)/30 = -0.90.$$

The within-sample sums of squares and products are

$$W_y = 7.60,$$
$$W_x = 6.00,$$
$$W_{xy} = 4.40.$$

The next step is the synthesis of subtotal sums of squares and products for the two components, linear and quadratic. The subtotal sums of squares and products for L are

$$L_y + W_y = 0.10 + 7.60 = 7.70,$$
$$L_x + W_x = 0.10 + 6.00 = 6.10,$$
$$L_{xy} + W_{xy} = 0.10 + 4.40 = 4.50.$$

Subtotal sums of squares and products for Q are

$$Q_y + W_y = 2.70 + 7.60 = 10.30,$$
$$Q_x + W_x = 0.30 + 6.00 = 6.30,$$
$$Q_{xy} + W_{xy} = -0.90 + 4.40 = 3.50.$$

The linear and quadratic subtotals must now be adjusted. L_e, the sum of squares of errors of prediction from the adjustment of the linear subtotal, is

$$(L_y + W_y) - \frac{(L_{xy} + W_{xy})^2}{(L_x + W_x)},$$

$$7.70 - (4.50)^2/6.10 = 4.38.$$

Q_e, the sum of squares of errors of prediction for the quadratic component, is

$$(Q_y + W_y) - \frac{(Q_{xy} + W_{xy})^2}{(Q_x + W_x)},$$

$$10.30 - (3.50)^2/6.30 = 8.36.$$

The sum of squares for the estimate of error, W_e, is obtained by adjusting the within-sample variability as follows:

$$W_e = W_y - \frac{W_{xy}^2}{W_x}$$

$$= 7.60 - (4.40)^2/6.00 = 4.37.$$

The discrepancy sums of squares, D_L and D_Q, are computed in the following manner:

$$D_L = L_e - W_e = 4.38 - 4.37 = 0.01,$$
$$D_Q = Q_e - W_e = 8.36 - 4.37 = 3.99.$$

Variances and F ratios for the tests of significance are presented in Table 14.4. The linear trend in the three means is not significant. The departures

Table 14.4
ANALYSIS OF COVARIANCE FOR THE SINGLE-FACTOR DESIGN WITH THREE LEVELS*

Component	SS	df	V	F
L	0.01	1	0.01	0.02
Q	3.99	1	3.99	9.98†
Error	4.37	11	0.40	

* Data in Table 14.3
† Null hypothesis rejected; F_c, the criterion value at the 0.05 level of significance is 4.84 for 1 and 11 df.

from linearity are significant, however, and the null hypothesis is rejected. The adjusted means are plotted in Fig. 14.5.

FOUR LEVELS

Given a single-factor design with four equally spaced levels of treatment, A_1, A_2, A_3, and A_4, the treatment sum of squares can be subdivided into three components: linear (L), quadratic (Q), and cubic (C). Each component is associated with one degree of freedom and can be tested for significance. The three components can be computed as follows:

$$L = \frac{(3A_4 + A_3 - A_2 - 3A_1)^2}{20n},$$

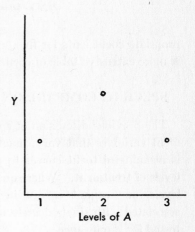

Fig. 14.5 Plot of the adjusted means for the single-factor example with three levels of treatment. (Data in Table 14.3)

where n is the number of subjects in a sample or, in the case of matched groups, becomes r, the number of groups.

$$Q = \frac{(A_4 - A_3 - A_2 + A_1)^2}{4n},$$

$$C = \frac{(A_4 - 3A_3 + 3A_2 - A_1)^2}{20n}.$$

The form of the analysis of variance for an experiment involving independent samples with no matching or adjusting is shown in Table 14.5. The ap-

Table 14.5
COMPONENTS OF VARIABILITY AND DEGREES OF FREEDOM FOR A SINGLE-FACTOR DESIGN WITH FOUR LEVELS OF TREATMENT IMPOSED ON FOUR SAMPLES

Component	df
Levels of A	3
Linear	1
Quadratic	1
Cubic	1
Error	$4(n - 1)$
Total	$N - 1$

n = number of subjects per sample
$N = 4n$ = total number of subjects

propriate coefficients for five and six levels are given by Snedecor[3] (p. 410). A more extensive table of coefficients is given by Fisher and Yates[2].

SPECIFIC COMPARISON OF QUALITIES

The previous discussion of specific comparisons has been limited to treatment variables that vary quantitatively, and thus to situations in which it is meaningful to fit curves to group means plotted against equally spaced levels of treatment. Where qualities of treatment are employed rather than levels, one cannot engage in curve fitting, but meaningful comparisons associated with single degrees of freedom can sometimes be formulated and tested for significance.

Two examples will be described in general terms.

1. A psychologist has three conditions which he wishes to employ in an experiment. Two of the conditions are qualities which he wishes to compare;

the third is a control condition or a standard condition with which he wishes to compare the first two. If we let A and B be the two qualities and S the control or standard, then two independent comparisons, each associated with one degree of freedom, can be written as follows

$$A - B,$$
$$2S - A - B.$$

If the letters are taken to be treatment sums of n observations, the sums of squares for the comparisons are

$$\frac{(A - B)^2}{2n},$$

$$\frac{(2S - A - B)^2}{6n},$$

from which variances are easily computed for evaluation in a test of significance.

2. An experiment is to be conducted having four conditions. There are two variations of A, A' and A''. There are also two variations of B, B' and B''. The psychologist wishes to compare A' with A'', B' with B'', and A with B. The three independent comparisons, each associated with one degree of freedom, are

$$A' - A'',$$
$$B' - B'',$$
$$A' + A'' - B' - B''.$$

Let each letter be the sum of n observations. Then the three sums of squares are

$$\frac{(A' - A'')^2}{2n},$$

$$\frac{(B' - B'')^2}{2n},$$

$$\frac{(A' + A'' - B' - B'')^2}{4n}.$$

Variances can be computed and tested for significance against the error variance appropriate to the design. Other possibilities for subdividing the over-all treatment sum of squares are discussed by Snedecor[3] (pp. 400-409), and Cochran and Cox[1] (pp. 59-64).

SUGGESTED READINGS

The rationale of specific comparisons in curve fitting is usually discussed in statistical literature under the general heading, "curvilinear regression," or the specific topic, "orthogonal polynomials." For advanced discussions, the interested student might consult the following sources:

Anderson, R.L., and Bancroft, T.A., *Statistical Theory in Research.* New York: McGraw-Hill Book Co., Inc., 1952.

Bennett, C.A., and Franklin, N.L., *Statistical Analysis in Chemistry and the Chemical Industry.* New York: John Wiley and Sons, Inc., 1954.

Cochran, W.G., and Cox, G.M., *Experimental Designs.* New York: John Wiley and Sons, Inc., 1950.

Fisher, R.A., *Statistical Methods for Research Workers.* New York: Hafner Publishing Co., Inc., 1948.

Grant, D.A., "Analysis-of-Variance Tests in the Analysis and Comparison of Curves," *Psychological Bulletin,* 53, 1956, 141-154.

Snedecor, G.W., *Statistical Methods.* Ames, Iowa: The Iowa State College Press, 1946.

REFERENCES

1. Cochran, W.G., and Cox, G.M., *Experimental Designs.* New York: John Wiley and Sons, Inc., 1950.
2. Fisher, R.A., and Yates, F., *Statistical Tables for Biological, Agricultural and Medical Research.* Edinburgh: Oliver & Boyd, Ltd., 1943.
3. Snedecor, G.W., *Statistical Methods.* Ames, Iowa: The Iowa State College Press, 1946.

SPECIFIC COMPARISONS
IN FACTORIAL DESIGNS

15

In factorial designs we have the problem of determining the nature of the function that expresses the relation between the dependent variable and two or more treatment variables. To represent graphically the results of a two-factor experiment, three dimensions must be accommodated. The three dimensions can be handled conveniently by two different plots in the same two-dimensional space.

Consider, as an example, the 2×2 design. The treatment plan consists of the four combinations: 1, a, b, and ab. If we let these symbols stand for the four means or sums of observations for the corresponding treatment combinations, then we can plot certain typical kinds of results as in Fig. 15.1. The ordinate is the dependent variable. The abscissa is the scale on which the two levels of A can be located. Two plots must be made. One is the plot of 1 and a, means or sums of observations made at the lower level of B. The other is the plot of b and ab, means or sums at the upper level of B.

We have seen before that the observations in a 2×2 design can be combined in various ways and then compared to provide information concerning the two main effects and the interaction. So it is that, in each of the graphs of Fig. 15.1, the heights of ordinates can be averaged or combined, and then

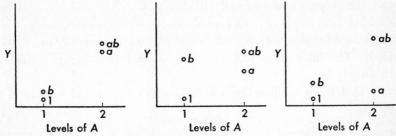

Fig. 15.1 Plots of means (or sums) for three different outcomes of a 2 x 2 design.

compared. In all three plots we see that the average height of points a and ab is greater than the average height of points 1 and b, and that the average height of points b and ab is greater than that of 1 and a. These two comparisons of average heights correspond to the two main effects, A and B, respectively.

A third comparison of the heights of points corresponds to the interaction AB. In the left graph of Fig. 15.1, the difference between ordinate values for a and 1 is the same as the difference between values for ab and b. That is to say, the difference between the two differences is zero and we conclude that there is no interaction. In the other two graphs, however, the two differences are not equal. In the middle graph, $(a - 1)$ is greater than $(ab - b)$. In the right graph, $(a - 1)$ is less than $(ab - b)$. In these two graphs, it would appear from a visual inspection that interaction is present.

In the 2×2 design, no conclusion can be reached as to the nature of the function. It is apparent, however, that, when interaction is present, the function relating response and levels of A for the lower level of B is different from the function for the upper level of B. When there is no interaction, as in the left graph, the function for the lower level of B may or may not be the same as that for the upper level. A decision cannot be made on this issue without additional evidence as to the location of intermediate points for each function.

THE 2×3 DESIGN

The treatment plan for a 2×3 design has been given in Plan 11.3. There are two factors, A and B. There are three levels of A and two levels of B. The plan thus prescribes six treatment combinations designated by the symbols in each cell.

In Table 15.1 are data for a 2×3 design. The three levels of A were equally spaced. Each treatment combination was imposed on a sample of three subjects and measures of response were obtained. The usual analysis gives two main effects, A and B, the interaction AB, and the estimate of error. We propose now a more detailed analysis. The main effect A can be subdivided into linear (L_a) and quadratic (Q_a) components, each of which can be tested for significance. The main effect B cannot, of course, be subdivided. The interaction AB, however, offers interesting possibilities for further analysis.

Note that there are two linear components of A, one at each level of B. They are

$$a_3b_2 - a_1b_2$$

and

$$a_3b_1 - a_1b_1.$$

Table 15.1

DATA FOR A 2 × 3 DESIGN WITH INDEPENDENT SAMPLES

	A_1	A_2	A_3
B_1	8 4 9	15 13 14	12 16 17
B_2	5 7 9	8 6 10	8 10 9

(Levels of A are equally spaced.)

The difference between these two differences indicates how much these two comparisons vary, depending on B.   That is,

$$(a_3b_2 - a_1b_2) - (a_3b_1 - a_1b_1)$$

or

$$a_3b_2 + a_1b_1 - a_1b_2 - a_3b_1$$

represents the interaction of L_a with B or "$L_a \times B$."

Note also that there are two quadratic components of A, one at each level of B.   They are

$$2a_2b_2 - a_1b_2 - a_3b_2$$

and

$$2a_2b_1 - a_1b_1 - a_3b_1.$$

The difference between these two comparisons,

$$(2a_2b_2 - a_1b_2 - a_3b_2) - (2a_2b_1 - a_1b_1 - a_3b_1)$$

or

$$2a_2b_2 + a_1b_1 + a_3b_1 - 2a_2b_1 - a_1b_2 - a_3b_2,$$

represents the interaction of Q_a and B, or "$Q_a \times B$."

The complete analysis of the data in Table 15.1 is described below.

The total sum of squares is

$$\Sigma Y^2 - C',$$
$$2040 - 180^2/18 = 240.$$

The within-sample or error sum of squares, obtained by applying the formula

$$\Sigma Y^2 - \frac{(\Sigma Y)^2}{n}$$

to each sample and combining the results, is 48.

The main effect, A, is computed as

$$\frac{A_1^2 + A_2^2 + A_3^2}{2n} - C',$$

$$(42^2 + 66^2 + 72^2)/6 - 1800 = 84.$$

The linear component of A, L_a, is

$$\frac{(A_3 - A_1)^2}{4n},$$

$$(72 - 42)^2/12 = 75$$

or

$$\frac{(a_3b_1 + a_3b_2 - a_1b_1 - a_1b_2)^2}{4n},$$

$$(45 + 27 - 21 - 21)^2/12 = 75.$$

The quadratic component of A, Q_a, is

$$\frac{(2A_2 - A_1 - A_3)^2}{12n},$$

$$(132 - 42 - 72)^2/36 = 9,$$

or

$$\frac{(2a_2b_1 + 2a_2b_2 - a_1b_1 - a_1b_2 - a_3b_1 - a_3b_2)^2}{12n}$$

$$(84 + 48 - 21 - 21 - 45 - 27)^2/36 = 9.$$

The main effect, B, is obtained as follows:

$$\frac{B_1^2 + B_2^2}{3n} - C',$$

$$(108^2 + 72^2)/9 - 1800 = 72.$$

The interaction, AB, computed by obtaining an interaction deviation for each sample mean by the formula

$$\bar{Y}_{jk} - \bar{Y}_{j.} - \bar{Y}_{.k} + \bar{Y}_{..},$$

squaring each deviation, summing, and weighting the sum for the sample size, is 36.

The interaction of L_a and B, or $L_a \times B$, is obtained in the following manner:

$$\frac{(a_3b_2 + a_1b_1 - a_1b_2 - a_3b_1)^2}{4n}$$

$$(27 + 21 - 45 - 21)^2/12 = 27.$$

The interaction of Q_a and B, or $Q_a \times B$, is

$$\frac{(2a_2b_2 + a_1b_1 + a_3b_1 - 2a_2b_1 - a_1b_2 - a_3b_2)}{12n},$$

$$(48 + 21 + 45 - 84 - 21 - 27)^2/36 = 9.$$

Table 15.2 gives a summary of the results of the analysis and the tests of significance. The main effect, B, is significant. We see, however, that the

Table 15.2
ANALYSIS OF VARIANCE FOR THE 2 × 3 EXAMPLE*

Component	SS	df	V	F
A	84	2		
L_a	75	1	75	18.75†
Q_a	9	1	9	2.25
B	72	1	72	18.00†
AB	36	2		
$L_a \times B$	27	1	27	6.75†
$Q_a \times B$	9	1	9	2.25
Error	48	12	4	
Total	240	17		

* Data in Table 15.1
† Null hypothesis rejected; F_c, the criterion value at the 0.05 level for 1 and 12 df is 4.75.

linear trend of *A* is significant and that departures from linearity are not.   In the interaction, it is the linear component of *A* which varies to produce the significant result.

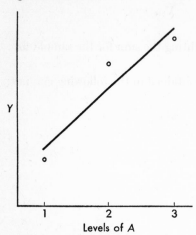

Fig. 15.2 Plot of the means of the three levels of *A* and the best-fitting regression line for the means. (Data in Table 15.1)

It is evident in Table 15.2 that the over-all effects, *A* and *AB*, were not tested.   The position taken by the author is that specific comparisons can be made when they are independent of one another and when their choice or formulation does not depend on the data obtained in the experiment.   The latter condition implies that the comparisons will be determined by the purpose of the experiment.   The position is also taken that over-all effects do not have to be significant for specific comparisons to be made.

Fig. 15.2 contains a plot of the means of the three levels of *A* and the best fitting regression line for those points. Fig. 15.3 shows a plot of means of the three levels of *A* for each level of *B*. The two linear trends apparently differ, an observation that is supported by the tests of significance.

THE 3 × 3 DESIGN

The last example of specific comparisons to be discussed here is the analysis appropriate to a 3 × 3 design. The treatment plan was given in Plan 11.4. There are three levels for each of two factors, with the nine combinations of treatments being indicated by the symbols in the cells.   Data for a 3 × 3 design are given in Table 15.3.   The nine treatment combinations were imposed on nine samples of three cases each.   The sample sums and the sums for columns and rows of the 3 × 3 classification are recorded in the lower part of Table 15.3.

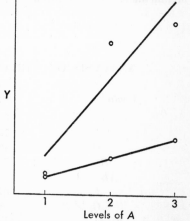

Fig. 15.3 Plot of the means of three levels of *A* for each level of *B* and the best-fitting regression line for each set. (Data in Table 15.1)

Table 15.3
DATA FOR A 3 × 3 DESIGN

	A_1	A_2	A_3
B_1	5	6	7
	2	6	12
	8	12	11
B_2	12	13	13
	3	7	16
	3	10	10
B_3	6	10	19
	11	15	13
	7	14	16

Sums

	A_1	A_2	A_3	
B_1	15	24	30	69
B_2	18	30	39	87
B_3	24	39	48	111
	57	93	117	267

(Note: Levels of A and B are equally spaced.)

The total variability can be analyzed into four components: two main effects, a first-order interaction, and an error sum of squares. The main effect A is associated with two degrees of freedom and can be further subdivided into a linear component, L_a, and a quadratic component, Q_a. The main effect, B, is also associated with two degrees of freedom and can be subdivided into linear and quadratic components, L_b and Q_b.

The interaction, AB, has four degrees of freedom and can be analyzed in terms of the linear and quadratic components of A and the way these vary over the three levels of B. The linear comparison for A can be made three times, once at each level of B. The variation in this linear comparison can be subdivided into linear and quadratic components, LL_a and QL_a, each with one degree of freedom. Likewise, there are three quadratic comparisons for A, one at each level of B. The variation in these three comparisons can be analyzed into linear and quadratic components, LQ_a and QQ_a. In this fashion, the over-all interaction, AB, is broken up into four parts, each associated with one degree of freedom.

Let us examine, first, the computation of the total sum of squares, the two main effects, the over-all interaction, and the error sum of squares before proceeding to the specific comparisons.

The total sum of squares is

$$\Sigma Y^2 - C'$$

$$3141 - 267^2/27 = 500.67.$$

If we let S be the sum of any sample, then the sum of squares for differences among the nine samples is

$$\frac{\Sigma S^2}{n} - C'$$

$$8847/3 - 267^2/27 = 308.67,$$

where the summation involves the nine squared sample sums.

Differences between the nine samples can be divided into the two main effects and the first-order interaction. The main effect, A, is computed as usual from the level sums given in Table 15.3 and the correction term, C':

$$(57^2 + 93^2 + 117^2)/9 - 2640.33 = 202.67.$$

B is computed in a similar fashion:

$$(69^2 + 87^2 + 111^2)/9 - 2640.33 = 98.67.$$

The Greco-Latin square, the square in two alphabets shown in Table 11.3, can be employed for classifying the sample sums and computing the inter-action, AB. We superimpose the square of Table 11.3 on the similar arrangement of sample sums in Table 15.3. If we attend only to the first alphabet, that is, to the number on the left in each cell, we can classify the sample sums as 1's, 2's, and 3's. The sums of the three classes thus obtained provide the basis for computing part of the interaction as follows:

$$(84^2 + 93^2 + 90^2)/9 - 2640.33 = 4.67.$$

Using the second alphabet in a similar manner, we obtain the other part of the interaction as

$$(93^2 + 87^2 + 87^2)/9 - 2640.33 = 2.67.$$

Combining these two parts, we obtain the whole interaction

$$AB = 4.67 + 2.67 = 7.34.$$

The error sum of squares is 192. It is found by computing the sum of squares for each sample and then combining these nine quantities.

We have said that the differences among the nine samples associated with eight degrees of freedom can be analyzed into eight components: L_a, Q_a, L_b, Q_b, LL_a, QL_a, LQ_a, and QQ_a. Computation of each of these eight components involves the sample sums, combined and compared in various ways. Since the eight comparisons differ only in the signs and coefficients employed with the sample sums, it is convenient to record the coefficients as in Table 15.4.

Table 15.4

COEFFICIENTS FOR THE SPECIFIC COMPARISONS IN THE 3 × 3 DESIGN

	a_1b_1	a_1b_2	a_1b_3	a_2b_1	a_2b_2	a_2b_3	a_3b_1	a_3b_2	a_3b_3	H
Sum	15	18	24	24	30	39	30	39	48	
L_a	-1	-1	-1	0	0	0	$+1$	$+1$	$+1$	6
Q_a	-1	-1	-1	$+2$	$+2$	$+2$	-1	-1	-1	18
L_b	-1	0	$+1$	-1	0	$+1$	-1	0	$+1$	6
Q_b	-1	$+2$	-1	-1	$+2$	-1	-1	$+2$	-1	18
LL_a	$+1$	0	-1	0	0	0	-1	0	$+1$	4
QL_a	$+1$	-2	$+1$	0	0	0	-1	$+2$	-1	12
LQ_a	$+1$	0	-1	-2	0	$+2$	$+1$	0	-1	12
QQ_a	$+1$	-2	$+1$	-2	$+4$	-2	$+1$	-2	$+1$	36

H = sum of the squares of coefficients in a row

The treatment combinations are listed across the upper margin. Below each combination is the corresponding sample sum from Table 15.3. On the left margin are the eight components of variability for the eight specific comparisons. In each row of the body of the table are the coefficients which are to be applied to the sample sums to make up a comparison. On the right margin of the table are values of H, the sum of the squares of the coefficients in a row. Any given component is computed by forming the comparison, squaring it, and dividing the square by $n H$, where n is the number of observations per sample.

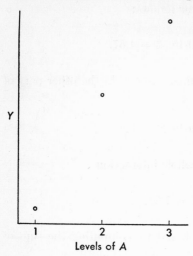

Fig. 15.4 Plot of the means of the three levels of A for the 3×3 example. (Data in Table 15.3)

The means of the three levels of A have been plotted in Fig. 15.4. The linear component of differences among the three means, L_a, is the variability predicted by the best fitting linear regression line. It is given by the computation

$$L_a = (30 + 39 + 48 - 15 - 18 - 24)^2/6(3) = 200.$$

Departure from linearity in the means of Fig. 15.4 is measured by Q_a:

$$Q_a = (48 + 60 + 78 - 15 - 18 - 24 - 30 - 39 - 48)^2/18(3) = 2.67.$$

Means of the three levels of B have been plotted in Fig. 15.5. The linear component, L_b, is computed as follows:

$$L_b = (24 + 39 + 48 - 15 - 24 - 30)^2/6(3) = 98.00.$$

The quadratic component of B is given by

$$Q_b = (36 + 60 + 78 - 15 - 24 - 30 - 24 - 39 - 48)^2/18(3) = 0.67.$$

Fig. 15.6 shows a plot of the nine sample means. Broken lines connect the three means for each level of B. Notice that we can distinguish a linear trend and departures from linearity at each level of B. The three linear trends vary, and we may wish to know if the specific components of this variation are significant. The three linear comparisons are

$$(30 - 15) = 15,$$
$$(39 - 18) = 21,$$
$$(48 - 24) = 24.$$

These three differences have been plotted against levels of B in the left part of Fig. 15.7. The linear component, LL_a, can be computed for these three differences from the comparison in Table 15.4:

$$LL_a = (48 - 24 - 30 + 15)^2/4(3) = 6.75.$$

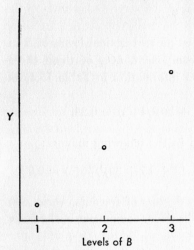

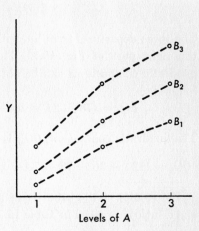

Fig. 15.5 Plot of the means of the three levels of B for the $3×3$ example. (Data in Table 15.3)

Fig. 15.6 Plot of the nine sample means from the $3×3$ example. Broken lines connect the three means for each level of B. (Data in Table 15.3)

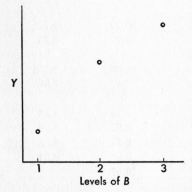

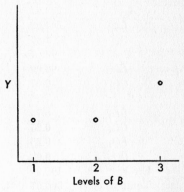

Fig. 15.7 The left plot is for the differences from the three linear comparisons in the $3×3$ example. The right plot is for the differences from the three quadratic comparisons. (Data in Table 15.3)

The quadratic component for these linear comparisons is

$$QL_a = (78 - 36 - 48 + 24 - 30 + 15)^2/12(3) = 0.25.$$

Refer again to Fig. 15.6. There is a departure from linearity at each level of B. The three comparisons are

$$2(24) - 15 - 30 = 3,$$
$$2(30) - 18 - 39 = 3,$$
$$2(39) - 24 - 48 = 6.$$

The three departures from linearity have been plotted against levels of B in the right part of Fig. 15.7. The linear component, LQ_a, of these three quadratic comparisons can be obtained from information in Table 15.4, as follows:

$$LQ_a = (78 - 24 - 48 - 48 + 15 + 30)^2/12(3) = 0.25.$$

The quadratic component, QQ_a, is computed in the following manner:

$$QQ_a = (120 - 36 - 78 - 78 + 24 + 48 - 48 + 15 + 30)^2/36(3) = 0.08.$$

The results of the subdivision along with degrees of freedom, variances, and F ratios are given in Table 15.5. Only the linear component of the main

Table 15.5

ANALYSIS OF VARIANCE OF THE 3 × 3 EXAMPLE*

Component	SS	df	V	F
A	202.67	2		
L_a	200.00	1	200.00	18.74†
Q_a	2.67	1	2.67	0.25
B	98.67	2		
L_b	98.00	1	98.00	9.18†
Q_b	0.67	1	0.67	0.06
AB	7.33	4		
LL_a	6.75	1	6.75	0.63
QL_a	0.25	1	0.25	0.02
LQ_a	0.25	1	0.25	0.02
QQ_a	0.08	1	0.08	0.01
Error	192.00	18	10.67	
Total	500.67	26		

* Data in Table 15.3
† Null hypothesis rejected; F_c at the 0.05 level for 1 and 18 df is 4.41.

effect, A, and the linear component of the main effect, B, are significant. We conclude that the dependent variable is a linear function of A and B with no interaction between the two treatments.

It should be apparent at this point that we could continue the elaboration of experimental designs much further, and even beyond all reasonable limits. The number of factors, as well as the number of levels for each factor, can be increased. Matching or adjusting could be incorporated. If matching was attempted with large groups, then confounding would probably be desirable. If adjusting was used, we might want to have more than one adjusting variable or to use a curvilinear regression. Although, in actual practice, designs somewhat more complicated than those discussed in the preceding pages are used fairly frequently, it has not seemed advisable to incorporate these more elaborate and complex designs in an introductory discussion.

As the student masters the basic principles of design, his skill in combining these principles in various ways to suit his requirements at any particular moment will increase. It is not possible to catalog and have available all possible variations in design and analysis. And even if it were possible, it is a risky business for the psychologist to select a design by scanning the pages of a text or a reference work. Too often the choice of a design is made on the basis of superficial correspondence between what the psychologist wants to do and what he finds in a book. It would be far better if he formulated the design and carried out the subsequent analysis with full understanding of what he was trying to do and how it might be accomplished in terms of basic principles.

IN RETROSPECT

The principal issues of experimental design, as they have been discussed here, can be subsumed under the headings: validity, precision, comprehensiveness, and hypothesis specificity. Validity has to do with the correspondence between the level of significance and the true probability of an error of the first kind. The main guarantee of validity is randomization. Precision refers to the magnitude of experimental error and is achieved, for the most part, by matching or adjusting procedures. Comprehensiveness is attained by employing more than one independent variable and evaluating interactions. Hypothesis specificity implies curve fitting in the attempt to determine the nature of the relation between a dependent variable and one or more independent variables.

EXTENSIONS

16

It is evident from previous discussions that experimental designs vary with respect to (a) the way in which a preliminary set of measures is used to increase precision, (b) the number of factors and number of levels of each, and (c) the specific comparisons that are appropriate to a design. We should note, however, that in previous discussions all designs had certain common characteristics. It was assumed that (a) the experimenter had only one population or supply on which he wished to experiment, (b) the treatment levels or qualities used were selected deliberately by the experimenter to suit his purposes, and (c) an experiment was performed only once for any given attempt at evaluation.

We shall consider next certain extensions of experimental planning and evaluation that have to do with incorporating two or more supplies in an experiment, selecting treatments randomly, and combining results of independent experiments.

TWO OR MORE SUPPLIES

Emphasis has already been given to the importance of the supply of materials employed in the experiment. The psychologist must give careful consideration to his choice of a supply of subjects and must describe it with care so that others will know to what kind of subjects the results apply. In many cases, a choice is difficult to make and the investigator eventually realizes that the experiment should be done on two or more different supplies. For example, there may be reason to expect that differences produced by certain conditions will not be the same for male and female subjects, and the investigator may feel obligated to include both sexes in the experiment rather than make an arbitrary choice of one.

Here are some other examples.

1. An industrial psychologist wishes to experiment with incentives in an effort to reduce absences from work. Since the same incentives may have different effects on workers in different job classifications, he may decide to use several occupational groups in the experiment.

2. An experimental psychologist plans an experiment on the effects of certain noxious stimuli on the emotional behavior of rats. He suspects that these effects vary, depending on the strain of animals used, so he intends using several strains in the investigation.

3. An educational psychologist formulates a design to test the effects of varied lectures in increasing the use of certain kinds of books in a university library. Because the relative effectiveness of the lectures may vary with the age and maturity of students, his design includes subjects from four supplies corresponding to the four undergraduate classes: freshman, sophomore, junior, and senior.

4. A clinical psychologist plans to impose two kinds of interview techniques on patients in a mental hospital and to measure the degree of confidentiality they exhibit in their responses. Since patients have already been assigned to wards on some selective basis, he decides to impose the two conditions on subjects obtained from each of several wards.

The general principle according to which two or more supplies are incorporated in the same experiment is that a sample of subjects is obtained from each supply and randomly subdivided into as many subsamples as there are treatments or treatment combinations. One subsample is then assigned to each treatment or combination of treatments.

In the analysis of the data, a classification is maintained for supplies and a component of variability is computed for differences between supplies. When the subjects representing each supply actually constitute a random sample from a larger number, it is appropriate to test the significance of the differences between supplies. In some cases, however, each supply consists of only a small number of subjects and the entire supply is employed in each instance and randomly assigned to subsamples and treatments. When each supply is exhausted by the selection of materials for an experiment, it is not appropriate to test the differences between supplies. That component of variability is simply set aside, but all other tests can be performed. It is important to note that the analysis proposed here assumes that all supplies have equal variances.

The arrangement of supplies, subsamples, and treatments for an experiment involving two supplies, P_g and P_h, and two levels of A is given in the upper part of Table 16.1. The components of variability and degrees of

Table 16.1
ARRANGEMENT OF SUPPLIES, SUBSAMPLES, AND TREATMENTS
FOR A SINGLE-FACTOR DESIGN, WITH COMPONENTS
OF VARIABILITY AND DEGREES OF FREEDOM

Levels of A

1   2

Supplies

P_g

P_h

(Each cell is a subsample of n cases)

Analysis

Component	*df*
Levels (A)	1
Supplies (P)	1*
Interaction (AP)	1
Error	$4(n-1)$†
Total	$N-1$

* Tested only when the subjects from each supply have been randomly selected
† The analysis assumes that both supplies have the same variance.

freedom are given in the lower part of the same table. Computation of the sum of squares for supplies is the same as for any classification. The rule is: Find the sum for each supply and square it; sum the squared sums and divide by the number of subjects from a supply; finally, subtract the appropriate correction term.   Interactions are computed by the usual methods.

The arrangement of supplies, subsamples, and treatment combinations for a 2×2 factorial design involving two supplies, P_g and P_h, is given in the upper part of Table 16.2. The components of variability and degrees of freedom are given in the lower part of the same table.

Table 16.2
ARRANGEMENT OF SUPPLIES, SUBSAMPLES, AND TREATMENT COMBINATIONS FOR A TWO-FACTOR DESIGN, WITH COMPONENTS OF VARIABILITY AND DEGREES OF FREEDOM

Treatment Combinations

	1	a	b	ab
P_g				
P_h				

Supplies

(Each cell is a subsample of n cases)

Analysis

Component	df
A	1
B	1
P	1*
AB	1
AP	1
BP	1
ABP	1
Error	$8(n-1)$†
Total	$N-1$

* Tested only when subjects from each supply have been randomly selected
† The analysis assumes that both supplies have a common variance.

Maintaining a classification for supplies makes it possible not only to test the differences between means of supplies but also to test the significance of the interaction of treatments and supplies. A significant interaction means that the treatment effects were not the same for the two or more supplies.

RANDOM CHOICE OF TREATMENTS

In most psychological experimentation, the choice of levels or qualities of treatment is determined by the experimenter's interests and purposes. In a few instances, when the experimenter's choice of a few qualities of treatment from a large number of possible ones is arbitrary, he may wish to interpret his findings with respect to what may be called the *population of treatments* and not limit his results to the particular treatments he employed in the experiment. When the qualities used are actually obtained by random selection, the experimenter can make an inference concerning the population of treatment effects. In the single-factor experiment with random selection of treatments, the test of significance is the same as that for the single-factor experiment with purposive selection of treatments. In factorial designs, the tests are somewhat different.

Before we examine the analysis and evaluation of certain simple designs incorporating random selection of treatments, let us consider two examples in which this extension of experimental design might be desirable.

1. An educator wishes to study the differences among prospective teachers of high school mathematics. He chooses four teachers from a large group; assigns, by random methods, 20 high school freshmen to each teacher; and gives the teachers the task of presenting a particular topic in elementary algebra. At the end of the period of instruction, the students are tested on the topic. The educator analyzes the data to determine whether or not there are differences among teachers in the results they obtain in the experiment. In such a study, the four teachers are the treatments and the results can be generalized to the population of teachers from which they were selected, if they were selected randomly.

2. An experiment is to be conducted to determine if there are differences among instructors who teach rifle marksmanship. Three instructors are chosen randomly from a large number of available instructors. Five rifles are also chosen randomly from a large number of available weapons. Thirty subjects for instruction are randomly selected from a supply and randomly assigned in equal numbers to the 15 combinations of instructors and rifles. A period of instruction is given the subjects and they are then tested for performance on the range. The experimenter can test for differences between instructors, differences between rifles, and their interaction. His results can be generalized to the supply of instructors and the supply of rifles.

The first example above involves one independent variable, where the qualities of treatment are the four teachers. The effects of the four teachers can be considered to be a random sample from a population of effects when the teachers have actually been selected from a large supply by some tested mechanical method.

Table 16.3 gives the arrangement of teachers and students, and a list of components of variability and degrees of freedom. The test of significance requires computation of F, the ratio of the treatment variance, V_t, to the error variance, V_e.

Table 16.3

ARRANGEMENT OF RANDOMLY SELECTED TREATMENTS AND SUBJECTS IN A SINGLE-VARIABLE DESIGN, WITH THE GENERAL FORM OF THE ANALYSIS

Teachers

A	*B*	*C*	*D*

(Each cell is a random group of n subjects)

Analysis

Component	df	V	F
Teachers	$c - 1$	V_t	V_t/V_e
Error	$c(n - 1)$	V_e	
Total	$N - c$		

In the example, c = number of teachers = 4, n = number of high school freshmen in each sample = 20, and N = total number of subjects = 80

The second example above involves two factors. One factor consists of a group of randomly selected instructors; the other consists of randomly selected rifles.

The arrangement of treatment combinations and random groups of subjects is given in the upper part of Table 16.4. In the lower part of the same table are listed components of variability, degrees of freedom, variances, and F ratios. Table 16.4 deserves careful study, because the F ratios shown there are not computed as they have been in other designs. The error term for the test of the interaction is the usual within-sample variance. The error term for each main effect is the interaction variance. The analysis suggested in Table 16.4 assumes that the number of treatments for each factor is quite small relative to the number in the population. When the number in the population is not much larger than the number employed, the error term is computed from the interaction and the within-sample sums of squares. For further discussion of this matter see Bennett and Franklin[1] (p. 373).

The occasion for random selection of treatments occurs infrequently in psychological research. When it does occur, it will sometimes be in connection with single-variable designs. When it occurs in factorial designs, it is much more likely to apply to one factor than to two or more. Consider the following example.

Table 16.4

ARRANGEMENT OF RANDOMLY SELECTED TREATMENTS AND SUBJECTS IN A TWO-FACTOR EXPERIMENT, WITH THE GENERAL ANALYSIS

Instructors

(Each cell is a random sample of n subjects)

Analysis

Component	df	V	F
Instructors (I)	$n_i - 1$	V_i	V_i/V_{ir}
Rifles (R)	$n_r - 1$	V_r	V_r/V_{ir}
Interaction (IR)	$(n_i - 1)(n_r - 1)$	V_{ir}	V_{ir}/V_e
Error	$n_i n_r (n - 1)$	V_e	
Total	$N - 1$		

In the example, n_i = number of instructors = 3, n_r = number of rifles = 5, n = number of subjects per sample = 2, N = total number of subjects = 30

A teacher is interested in conducting an experiment on beginners in a typing class. He has two kinds of practice schedules, one with practice massed at a few points in time, the other with practice distributed over numerous points in the same time period. He plans to assign 20 students randomly to the two conditions of practice. It is not feasible to perform the experiment with only one typewriter so he chooses five machines from more than a hundred available machines and assigns randomly the ten students in each condition to the five machines. He has thereby arranged his subjects in ten random groups of two, each such pair assigned randomly to a particular machine and a particular condition of practice.

The analysis appropriate to the typing experiment includes tests of significance for the two main effects, kind of practice schedule and machine, and the interaction of schedules and machines. Because practice schedules have been purposively selected and machines have been randomly selected, the F ratios for the two main effects are not computed in the same way.

The upper part of Table 16.5 shows the arrangement of treatment combinations and random groups of subjects. The lower part of the same table contains a summary of the analysis. Note that the interaction variance is

Table 16.5
ARRANGEMENT OF RANDOMLY AND PURPOSIVELY SELECTED TREATMENTS IN A TWO-FACTOR EXPERIMENT, WITH THE APPROPRIATE ANALYSIS

Practice Schedules

A   B

Machines 1
          2
          3
          4
          5

(Each cell is a sample of n subjects)

Analysis

Component	df	V	F
Practice schedules (P)	$n_p - 1$	V_p	V_p/V_{pm}
Machines (M)	$n_m - 1$	V_m	V_m/V_e
Interaction (PM)	$(n_p - 1)(n_m - 1)$	V_{pm}	V_{pm}/V_e
Error	$n_p n_m(n - 1)$	V_e	
Total	$N - 1$		

In the example, n_p = number of practice schedules = 2, n_m = number of typewriters = 5, n = number of subjects per sample = 2, and N = total number of subjects = 20 compared with the usual error term, the within-sample variance. The main effect for machines is also evaluated by comparison with the within-sample variance. The main effect for practice, on the other hand, is compared with the interaction variance.

For additional information about designs involving randomly selected treatments, see Bennett and Franklin.[1]

COMBINING RESULTS

When an investigator has data for two or more experiments bearing on the same question or problem, he usually prefers combining the results by some statistical method, the terms of which are made explicit, over combining them on the basis of an interpretive judgment, in which it may be difficult or impossible to discern the principle involved. There are two quite satisfactory methods of combining results that are employed occasionally in psychology. Both methods of combining assume that the two or more sets of data are independent. The operational guarantees that they will be independent lie in the use of a separate group of subjects for each experiment and in the random assignment of subjects within each group to the conditions of the experiment.

We shall give two examples of situations in which the first of the two methods would be desirable.

1. An investigator performs an experiment and, after some lapse of time, repeats the experiment on different subjects. His reason for doing two experiments at different times instead of one large experiment may arise from certain practical considerations having to do with the availability of space and equipment, or other problems of managing a large experiment. In this example, the two experiments are identifiable in terms of the time at which each was carried out. We might therefore identify the experiments as T_1 and T_2.

2. The scheduling, treatment, and measurement of some desired number of subjects requires the services of two experimenters, so the subjects are divided into two equal groups and randomly assigned, within each group, to the conditions of the experiment. There are, then, really two complete experiments, identifiable in terms of the experimenter conducting each of them as E_1 and E_2.

The method of combining results is essentially the same for both of these examples. A new classification can be introduced in the analysis of the data. In the first example, the new classification is based on the times of conducting the experiment. In the second example, the classification is based on experimenters. A corresponding component of variability can be computed. It is usually not important and often not correct to test this component for significance. If the experimenter can show that the difference between experiments is in fact subject to random errors and that an estimate of these errors is available, then the differences between experiments can be tested, We shall assume that no particular importance attaches to this difference, except that it may be a bias which should be eliminated, and that it should simply be computed and set aside.

Table 16.6 shows the arrangement of subjects and treatments for two experiments conducted at different times, T_1 and T_2. Each experiment involves three levels of independent variable A and three random groups of n subjects. In the lower part of Table 16.6, the analysis is indicated.

Table 16.6

COMBINING THE RESULTS OF TWO EXPERIMENTS PERFORMED AT DIFFERENT TIMES

Levels of A

(Each cell is a sample of n subjects)

Analysis

Component	df
A	2
L_a	1
Q_a	1
T	1*
AT	2
$L_a \times T$	1
$Q_a \times T$	1
Error	$6(n-1)$
Total	$N-1$

* No test of significance if randomization is restricted to each row

The arrangement of subjects and treatment combinations for two 2×2 factorial experiments is given in Table 16.7. The two experiments were conducted by different individuals, E_1 and E_2, and employed different groups of

Table 16.7
COMBINING THE RESULTS OF TWO EXPERIMENTS
PERFORMED BY DIFFERENT EXPERIMENTERS

Treatment Combinations

	1	a	b	ab
E_1				
E_2				

(Each cell is a sample of n subjects)

Analysis

Component	df
A	1
B	1
E	1*
AB	1
AE	1
BE	1
ABE	1
Error	$8(n - 1)$
Total	$N - 1$

* No test of significance if randomization is restricted to each row

subjects. Both experiments involved two levels of A and two levels of B, yielding four treatment combinations. The analysis is also given in Table 16.7

Computation of components of variability in these designs follows the usual practices. The components for T in Table 16.6 and for E in Table 16.7 are computed by finding the class or row sums, squaring them, combining the squares, dividing by the number of observations in the class, and subtracting the correction term. Interaction sums of squares can be computed by the methods given earlier.

Instead of maintaining a separate classification for experimenters, it is possible to deliberately confound differences between experimenters with a treatment effect, the evaluation of which is not considered to be important in that experiment. For example, in a $2 \times 2 \times 2$ factorial experiment with random samples, the second order interaction, ABC, could be confounded with experimenters. The design would require eight samples making a total of $8n$ subjects. Four samples and one experimenter would be assigned to the four treatment combinations: a, b, c, and abc; the remaining four samples and the second experimenter would be assigned to the combinations 1, ab, ac, and bc. The analysis would produce three main effects, A, B and C; three first-order interactions, AB, AC and BC; and a seventh component representing the confounded second-order interaction, ABC, and experimenter differences. In addition, of course, there would be a component for error. Only the main effects and first-order interactions would be tested for significance.

The advantages of confounding experimenters with a treatment effect are that each experimenter would then handle fewer conditions and that, since the treatment groups would be fewer and larger than when a separate classification is maintained for experimenters, fewer degrees of freedom would be lost in the estimate of error. It should be noted that this use of confounding assumes that there are no treatment and experimenter interactions.

The second method of combining results is particularly useful when there is some objection to pooling observations from two or more experiments and subjecting them to the same arithmetic analysis. For example, a psychologist may carry out an experiment in which he uses a certain test of mathematical ability as the dependent variable. He repeats the experiment at a later date but believes that it is advisable to use a parallel form of the test which, unfortunately, may yield scores not exactly comparable to those obtained in the earlier experiment.

If the results of each experiment, evaluated separately, are significant, then there is no problem in interpreting the combined results. When the results vary from one experiment to the other, a given component being significant in one instance and not in the other, or when both fail by a narrow margin to equal or exceed the criterion value, an inspection of the probabilities associated with the outcomes will not be satisfactory as a basis for making a decision.

A test described by Fisher[2] and discussed at length by Jones and Fiske[4] provides a solution to the problem of combining results under these circumstances. The test is essentially a means of assessing the significance of a joint probability. The investigator determines the probability associated with the result of each of two or more independent experiments. Each probability value can be transformed to a chi-square value with two degrees of freedom. The sum of these chi-square values is itself distributed as chi square with a number of degrees of freedom equal to twice the number of independent probability values to be combined.

The transformation of a probability value to a chi-square value is given by the equation

$$\chi^2 = -2(\log_e P).$$

The composite chi square is given by the formula

$$\chi^2{}_{cp} = -2\Sigma(\log_e P).$$

The transformation is facilitated by the use of tables published by Gordon, Loveland, and Cureton[3].

An example showing how probabilities are combined will be worked out below. Let us suppose that an experimenter has results from two experiments and has analyzed them separately, as indicated in Table 16.8. We note that the linear component is significant at the 0.05 level ($P = 0.025$) in

Table 16.8
RESULTS OF ANALYZING TWO EXPERIMENTS SEPARATELY

Experiment I

Component	SS	df	V	F
Levels of A	17.91	2		
L_a	11.82	1	11.82	5.63*
Q_a	6.09	1	6.09	2.90†
Error	56.70	27	2.10	
Total	74.61	29		

* P = probability associated with F = 0.025
† P = probability associated with F = 0.100

Experiment II

Component	SS	df	V	F
Levels of A	9.24	2		
L_a	2.99	1	2.99	1.38*
Q_a	6.25	1	6.25	2.88†
Error	65.10	30	2.17	
Total	74.34	32		

* P = probability associated with F = 0.250
† P = probability associated with F = 0.100

experiment I but is not significant in experiment II ($P = 0.250$). The quadratic component is not significant in either experiment, since the probability associated with F is, in each instance, 0.10.

Consider the linear component first. For experiment I,

$$P = 0.025; \log_e P = 6.311 - 10.$$

For experiment II,

$$P = 0.250; \log_e P = 8.614 - 10.$$

We compute the composite chi square by

$$\chi^2_{cp} = -2 \Sigma (\log_e P)$$

$$= -2(14.925 - 20)$$

$$= -2(-5.075)$$

$$= 10.150.$$

The criterion value of chi square at the 0.05 level for four degrees of freedom is 9.488. Since the composite chi square exceeds this criterion value, the null hypothesis is rejected and the linear component is found to be significant.

Consider next the quadratic component. For experiment I,

$$P = 0.100; \log_e P = 7.697 - 10.$$

For experiment II,

$$P = 0.100; \log_e P = 7.697 - 10.$$

The composite chi square is

$$\chi^2_{cp} = -2(15.394 - 20)$$

$$= -2(-4.606)$$

$$= 9.212.$$

The criterion value of chi square is again 9.488. In this instance the composite chi square is not significant.

REFERENCES

1. Bennett, C.A., and Franklin, N.L., *Statistical Analysis in Chemistry and the Chemical Industry*. New York: John Wiley & Sons, Inc., 1954.
2. Fisher, R.A., *Statistical Methods for Research Workers*. New York: Hafner Publishing Company, Inc., 1948, p. 100.
3. Gordon, M.H., Loveland, E.H., and Cureton, E.E., "An Extended Table of Chi Square for Two Degrees of Freedom, for Use in Combining Probabilities from Independent Samples." *Psychometrika*, 1952, 17, 311–316.
4. Jones, L.V., and Fiske, D.W., "Models for Testing the Significance of Combined Results." *Psychological Bulletin*, 1953, 50, 375–381.

SPECIAL PROBLEMS

17

Three problems will be considered in this chapter. The first has to do with the relative effectiveness of methods commonly used to increase the precision of experiments. The second problem is that of unequal sample sizes and missing observations. The third concerns certain tempting but fallacious methods of matching which are occasionally encountered in educational and psychological research.

PRECISION

In previous chapters, we noted that the precision of psychological experiments can be increased by methods requiring preliminary measurement of subjects or by repeated treatment of the same subjects. In practice, the experimenter's choice of a procedure has often been influenced by practical considerations or by his own intuitive notions regarding the relative effectiveness of the different methods. It is possible, however, to compare the several procedures, in an objective manner, with respect to their effectiveness in increasing precision, thereby placing the selection of a design on a sounder footing.

Consider an experiment in which

c = number of treatments,

n = number of observations per treatment,

$N = cn$ = total number of observations on the dependent variable,

X = preliminary measure on all subjects under uniform conditions,

Y = measure on the dependent variable under conditions of the experiment,

ρ = linear correlation between X and Y in a normal bivariate population.

235

When $c = 2$, the experimental comparison is a difference between means, which difference is subject to sampling variation. The variance of the sampling distribution can be taken as a measure of the lack of precision. We shall follow D. R. Cox[2] in calling this variance the *true imprecision*. The variance of the difference between two means can be expressed in terms of the variance of a single random observation, that is, in terms of the population variance. If we let σ_y^2 be the variance of a random observation on the dependent variable, then $2\sigma_y^2$ is the variance of a difference between two random observations from the same population. Then the variance of a mean difference, the true imprecision for a design employing two random samples and evaluated by a simple analysis of variance, is

$$\frac{2\sigma_y^2}{n}.$$

When $c > 2$, we may take the average imprecision for all possible comparisons. The average imprecision for the analysis of variance applied to independent samples is again $2\sigma_y^2/n$.

Four commonly used methods of increasing the precision of an experiment were presented earlier. Three of the methods require pre-experimental measurement of subjects under uniform conditions. The fourth method requires that subjects appear in all c conditions of the experiment.

GAINS

The experimenter obtains c random samples of subjects with n units per sample. Before imposition of treatments, subjects are measured on X, a variable assumed to be linearly correlated with the dependent variable. Treatments are then imposed and subjects are measured on Y. A difference or gain, $(Y - X)$, is computed for each subject. The experiment can be evaluated by an analysis of variance of the difference or gain scores. The analysis yields treatment and error components of variability.

The experimental comparison is a difference between mean differences. The variance of the difference, $(Y - X)$, is

$$\sigma_{y-x}^2 = \sigma_y^2 - 2\rho\sigma_y\sigma_x + \sigma_x^2.$$

The variance of the difference between two independent differences is $2\sigma_{y-x}^2$. When $\sigma_y^2 = \sigma_x^2$, a reasonable assumption if X and Y are actually the same variables as is often the case when gains are employed, then

$$2\sigma_{y-x}^2 = 4\sigma_y^2(1 - \rho).$$

The variance of the difference between mean differences or the true imprecision for gains is

$$\frac{4\sigma_y^2}{n}(1 - \rho).$$

ADJUSTING

The experimenter needs c random samples of n units each. Prior to differential treatment, all subjects are measured on X, which is assumed to be linearly correlated with Y. Treatments are imposed and observations made on Y. The experiment is evaluated by an analysis of covariance.

The experimental comparison is a function of adjusted means. Sample means on Y are adjusted for pre-experimental inequalities on X by means of the regression of Y on X, as estimated from the data. If ρ were known, the true imprecision would be

$$\frac{2\sigma_y^2}{n}(1 - \rho^2).$$

D. R. Cox[2] has shown that the true imprecision for the analysis of covariance when the regression must be estimated from the data, is

$$\frac{(N - c - 1)}{(N - c - 2)} \frac{2\sigma_y^2}{n}(1 - \rho^2).$$

MATCHING

A total sample of N cases is required. Pre-experimental measures on X are obtained on all subjects under uniform conditions. Subjects are then ranked and formed into n groups of c units each. Within each matched group subjects are randomly assigned to the c treatments. Treatments are then imposed and subjects are measured on the dependent variable. The analysis of variance yields components for treatment, error, and group differences.

The experimental comparison is a mean within-group difference. D. R. Cox[2] found the true imprecision for matching designs to be

$$\frac{2\sigma_y^2}{n}[1 - \rho^2(1 - W)],$$

where $W =$ expected mean square of X within groups, divided by σ_x^2. Values of W can be computed from tables compiled by Teichroew[6].

REPEATED TREATMENT

The experimenter obtains a total sample of (N/c) subjects. Treatments are randomly assigned to the c occasions on which each subject appears in the experiment. The variability in the N observations on Y can be analyzed into three components: treatment, error, and differences among subjects.

The experimental comparison is a mean, within-subject difference. The variance of a difference, $(Y - X)$, when Y and X are actually the same variable, can be written

$$\sigma_y^2 - 2\rho\sigma_y\sigma_y + \sigma_y^2 = 2\sigma_y^2(1 - \rho).$$

The true imprecision for a design involving repeated treatment is, therefore,

$$\frac{2\sigma_y^2}{n}(1 - \rho).$$

ERROR DEGREES OF FREEDOM

The variance of the experimental comparison is not entirely satisfactory as the basis for comparing designs because they differ in another important respect. The number of degrees of freedom used in computing the error variance is not the same in the four designs. We should take account of the number of degrees of freedom in the error term, because it has consequences for the length of confidence intervals and for the sensitivity of the experiment. We can do so by computing the *apparent imprecision* which is defined as the true imprecision multiplied by the factor

$$\frac{df + 3}{df + 1},$$

where df = the number of degrees of freedom for error. For a discussion of this factor, see D. R. Cox[2] and Cochran and G. M. Cox[1] (pp. 26-29).

Degrees of freedom used in computing the error variance for the simple analysis of variance and for the four designs under consideration are:

Design	df
Simple analysis of variance	$N - c$
Gains	$N - c$
Adjusting	$N - c - 1$
Matching*	$(c - 1)(n - 1)$
Repeated treatment	$(c - 1)(n - 1)$

* Note that n, the number of observations per treatment, is equal to r, the number of matched groups.

COMPARISON OF DESIGNS

There are a number of ways in which the relative effectiveness of the several designs in increasing precision might be determined or expressed. The one we shall use here seems to be straightforward and meaningful. It is the ratio of two apparent imprecisions, the apparent imprecision for the design to be evaluated divided by the apparent imprecision for the simple analysis of variance. The apparent imprecision ratio can be interpreted in the following manner: When the ratio is greater than unity, the error in the estimated comparison is greater for the method in question than it is in the simple analysis of variance and use of that particular method entails a loss of precision. When the ratio is less than unity, the method in question gives an increase in precision. When the ratio is exactly unity, there is no difference between the method in question and the simple analysis of variance.

Values of the apparent imprecision ratio have been computed and are tabled below for three variations in the number of treatments and observations. Table 17.1 gives ratios for an experiment in which $c = 2$ and $n = 10$,

Table 17.1
APPARENT IMPRECISION RATIOS FOR $c = 2$, $n = 10$ AND VARIED VALUES OF ρ

	ρ										
	0.00	0.10	0.20	0.30	0.40	0.50	0.60	0.70	0.80	0.90	1.00
Gains	2 000	1 800	1 600	1 400	1 200	1 000	800	600	400	200	000
Adjusting	1 068	1 057	1 025	972	897	801	684	545	384	203	000
Matching	1 086	1 076	1 045	994	922	830	717	584	431	256	062
Repeated treatment	1 086	977	869	760	652	543	434	326	217	109	000

$W = 0.0570$
Ratios should be read with three decimal places

Table 17.2
APPARENT IMPRECISION RATIOS FOR $c = 2$, $n = 6$ AND VARIED VALUES OF ρ

	ρ										
	0.00	0.10	0.20	0.30	0.40	0.50	0.60	0.70	0.80	0.90	1.00
Gains	2 000	1 800	1 600	1 400	1 200	1 000	800	600	400	200	000
Adjusting	1 142	1 131	1 097	1 040	960	857	731	583	411	217	000
Matching	1 128	1 118	1 088	1 038	968	878	767	637	486	316	126
Repeated treatment	1 128	1 015	903	790	677	564	451	338	226	113	000

$W = 0.1112$
Ratios should be read with three decimal places

Table 17.3

**APPARENT IMPRECISION RATIOS FOR $c = 4$, $n = 5$ AND VARIED
VALUES OF ρ**

	ρ										
	0.00	0.10	0.20	0.30	0.40	0.50	0.60	0.70	0.80	0.90	1.00
Gains	2 000	1 800	1 600	1 400	1 200	1 000	800	600	400	<u>200</u>	000
Adjusting	1 078	1 068	1 035	981	906	809	<u>690</u>	<u>550</u>	<u>388</u>	205	000
Matching	1 032	1 023	<u>996</u>	<u>951</u>	<u>887</u>	<u>806</u>	706	588	452	298	125
Repeated treatment	1 032	929	826	723	619	516	413	310	206	103	000

$W = 0.1214$

Ratios should be read with three decimal places

a case which occurs frequently in practice. Table 17.2 gives ratios for $c = 2$ and $n = 6$, a case very close to the lower limit of size for a worthwhile experiment. As n increases, the ratio for repeated treatment approaches $(1 - \rho)$, while the ratios for adjusting and matching approach $(1 - \rho^2)$. The ratio for gains is $2(1 - \rho)$.

Table 17.3 gives apparent imprecision ratios for an experiment in which $c = 4$ and $n = 5$.

DISCUSSION

Values of the apparent imprecision ratio in the first column of each table indicate that, when $\rho = 0$, imprecision is greater for all four methods than it is for a simple analysis of variance. Ratios in the fourth row of each of the three tables show that repeated treatment is generally superior to the other three methods. Since repeated treatment and measurement are, in many instances, precluded by the enduring changes they effect, the actual advantage of the method is not as great as it appears in the tables.

Because repeated treatment is often not feasible, it is worthwhile to examine separately the ratios for gains, adjusting, and matching. In all three tables, the lowest entry in each column has been underlined (disregarding the fourth row), where that entry is less than unity. In Tables 17.1 and 17.2, the greatest advantage in precision is thus found to be given by the analysis of covariance for values of ρ in the middle range. For very high values of ρ, the use of gains gives the greatest precision.

In Table 17.3, the advantage shifts twice. It lies with matching for values of ρ from 0.20 to 0.50, with adjusting for values of ρ from 0.60 to 0.80, and with gains when ρ is 0.90 or higher. For a fixed N, the relation between ratios for covariance and those for matching depends upon the number of treatments. When $c = 2$ and $n = N/2$, the disparity in error degrees of freedom is greatest, with the covariance analysis having the advantage of the larger number. At the same time, W has its smallest value. When $c = N/2$ and $n = 2$, both analyses have the same number of error degrees of freedom, while W takes its largest value.

It is interesting to note that the apparent imprecision ratio for gains does not depend on the size of samples. Values of the ratio in the first row of each table show that the use of gains entails a loss of precision when ρ is less than 0.50. Ratios for gains have been computed assuming that $\sigma_y^2 = \sigma_x^2$. The situation is somewhat more complex when the two variances are not equal. The true imprecision is

$$\frac{2\sigma_{y-x}^2}{n} = \frac{2(\sigma_y^2 - 2\rho\sigma_y\sigma_x + \sigma_x^2)}{n}.$$

The apparent imprecision ratio is

$$1 - \frac{2\rho\sigma_x}{\sigma_y} + \frac{\sigma_x^2}{\sigma_y^2}.$$

It is evident that the ratio will be less than unity when $\sigma_x/\sigma_y < 2\rho$. For a more extensive discussion of this matter, see Gourlay[4] and D. R. Cox.[2]

The differences in precision between adjusting and matching do not appear to be very large. If they are not judged to be important, other considerations may quite properly influence the experimenter's choice of a method. Matching has the disadvantage that a lapse of time between initial measurement and imposition of treatments is required for ranking, grouping, and random assigning of subjects. The covariance method can often be used with the imposition of treatments following immediately the initial measurement. Matching has the advantage that its effectiveness does not depend on linearity of regression. Any smooth regression is satisfactory for matching methods. Of course, curvilinear regression can be employed in the adjusting of analysis of covariance, but only with a reduction in the number of error degrees of freedom. Adjusting for differences on two or more variables simultaneously by means of multiple regression is also possible in the covariance approach.

When repeated treatment is possible, there is, in addition to the increase in precision, another considerable advantage. No preliminary measurement is required and only N/c subjects are needed.

Feldt[3] has published a discussion of these issues. The student may be interested in referring to his article.

UNEQUAL SAMPLE SIZES

In single-factor experiments with random samples of subjects, variation in sample size must be taken into consideration in the computation, but it presents no great difficulty. Within-sample sums of squares are computed using the appropriate n for each sample, that is, n_k for the kth sample. If we let S_k be the sum of the values in the kth sample, then the formula for the between-sample sum of squares is

$$\sum \frac{S_k^2}{n_k} - C',$$

where C' is the usual correction term. This computation has already been described on page 38.

In factorial designs, we can distinguish two kinds of inequality in sample size. In the one kind, the sample sizes are said to be *proportional*. In the other, they are said to be *disproportional*.

Proportionality obtains in a rectangular table of frequencies when any cell entry, n_{jk}, is given by the product of the marginal frequencies, $n_{j.}$ and $n_{.k}$, divided by the total frequency, N. That is, n_{jk} should equal

$$\frac{(n_{j.})(n_{.k})}{N}.$$

In Table 17.4, two 2×3 arrangements of sample sizes are shown. The upper one satisfies the criterion of proportionality. The lower one does not and is, therefore, an instance of disproportionality.

Table 17.4

**PROPORTIONAL AND DISPROPORTIONAL CELL FREQUENCIES
IN A 2×3 DESIGN**

Proportionality

	A_1	A_2	A_3	
B_1	8	9	12	29
B_2	16	18	24	58
	24	27	36	87

Disproportionality

	A_1	A_2	A_3	
B_1	8	9	13	30
B_2	15	18	21	54
	23	27	34	84

Unequal but proportional sample sizes can be dealt with rather easily. The two factors are independent, so the usual computing procedures can be employed for the two main effects, A and B. If we let B_j be the sum of values for the jth level of B, then the sum of squares is

$$\sum \frac{B_j^2}{n_{j.}} - C'.$$

If we let A_k be the sum for the kth level of A, then that sum of squares is

$$\sum \frac{A_k^2}{n_{.k}} - C'.$$

The sum of squares for AB must be computed by subtraction. If we let S_{jk} be the sample sum for the jth level of B and the kth level of A, then the between-sample sum of squares is

$$\sum \frac{S_{jk}^2}{n_{jk}} - C'.$$

Subtracting the sums of squares for A and B from the between-sample sum of squares yields the interaction sum of squares, AB. Degrees of freedom are as follows: for A, $(n_a - 1)$; for B, $(n_b - 1)$; for AB, $(n_a - 1)(n_b - 1)$.

Disproportionality is accompanied by forbidding computational difficulties. Disproportionality entails nonindependence of factors and their effects, and the usual computing procedures cannot be employed. No attempt will be made here to describe the rationale underlying the appropriate procedures. Only the steps in computing will be given.

Let n_a = number of levels of A and n_b = number of levels of B. Further, let n_{jk} be the sample size for the jth level of B and the kth level of A. We define the following quantities anew:

$$n_{.k} = \frac{n_b^2}{\sum_j (1/n_{jk})},$$

$$N_k = \sum n_{.k},$$

$$\bar{Y}_{.k} = \frac{\sum_j \bar{Y}_{jk}}{n_b}.$$

Then the sum of squares for A is given by

$$\sum_k n_{.k} \bar{Y}_{.k}^2 - C_k',$$

where

$$C_k' = \frac{\left(\sum_k n_{.k} \bar{Y}_{.k}\right)^2}{N_k}.$$

In a similar fashion, we also define

$$n_{j.} = \frac{n_a^2}{\sum_k (1/n_{jk})},$$

$$N_j = \sum n_{j.},$$

$$\bar{Y}_{j.} = \frac{\sum_k \bar{Y}_{jk}}{n_a}.$$

Then the sum of squares for B is

$$\sum_j n_{j.} \bar{Y}_{j.}^2 - C_j',$$

where

$$C_j' = \frac{\left(\sum_j n_{j.} \bar{Y}_{j.}\right)}{N_j}.$$

Degrees of freedom for A and B are the usual $(n_a - 1)$ and $(n_b - 1)$. The error variance is obtained by combining the within-sample sums of squares and dividing by $(N - n_a n_b)$.

The interaction sum of squares cannot be computed by a simple subtraction of the main effects from the between-sample sum of squares. It is necessary to compute first the maximum likelihood estimates of the A-effects and the B-effects. These estimates are obtained by the solution of a set of $(n_a + n_b + 1)$ equations. The estimates can then be used to effect an adjustment of the between-sample sum of squares, which adjustment gives the interaction sum of squares.

The equations which must be solved will not be given here. They can be found in Kenney and Keeping[5] (p. 267). The adjustment which employs the maximum likelihood estimates of the treatment effects is given by the same authors (pp. 270-271). Degrees of freedom for the interaction AB are $(n_a - 1)(n_b - 1)$.

It should be apparent that disproportionality is something to be avoided if at all possible. Unfortunately, many students learn of the difficulties only after completing their experiments. When they attempt the analysis, they discover that the sums of squares computed in the usual manner are not additive. Their checks do not work out. They finally learn of the correct but difficult computing procedures that are their only recourse.

MISSING VALUES

In matched-group designs, it sometimes happens that a subject in one of the groups drops out of the experiment leaving a vacant cell in the $(r \times c)$ tabulation of data. It is possible to estimate the missing value and thereby utilize the available information for that group.

If we let

Y_{jk} = the missing value for the jth group and the kth treatment,

A'_k = the treatment sum of available observations,

G'_j = the group sum of available observations,

T' = the grand total for all available observations,

then we can compute Y'_{jk}, a first estimate of Y_{jk} by

$$Y'_{jk} = \frac{rG'_j + cA'_k - T'}{(c - 1)(r - 1)}. \qquad (17.1)$$

Y'_{jk} is the estimate which minimizes the residual or error sum of squares.

Y'_{jk} is next entered in the vacant cell and the treatment and residual sum of squares are computed. Before testing the significance of the treatment effects, however, the treatment sum of squares must be adjusted. We first compute

$$U = \frac{c - 1}{c}(Y'_{jk} - Y''_{jk})^2,$$

where Y''_{jk} is a second estimate of Y_{jk} obtained by

$$Y''_{jk} = \frac{G'_j}{c-1}$$

Y''_{jk} is an estimate which minimizes the combined treatment and error sum of squares.

The adjustment is

$$A - U,$$

where A is the treatment sum of squares. Degrees of freedom for A are $(c-1)$ and for error are $(c-1)(r-1) -1$.

When two values are missing, each is estimated in terms of the other by formula (17.1) above. The two equations in two unknowns can then be solved for the first estimates. Treatment and residual sums of squares are computed next. The treatment sum of squares is then adjusted. Details of the computation and an example are given by Kenney and Keeping[5] (pp. 272-274).

FALLACIOUS MATCHING

The matching of subjects to reduce error in the experimental comparisons is an important method of increasing the precision of a design. That the merits of the correct matching procedure are not always understood by the investigator is apparent in certain attempts at matching which are seriously at fault.

One of the oldest forms of fallacious matching involves the arrangement of treatment groups so as to equalize, as much as possible, the means and variances of the groups on a preliminary set of measures. The experimenter may start with random groups. Subjects are measured under uniform conditions on a variable believed to be correlated with the dependent variable. When the experimenter examines these preliminary measures, he very likely discovers that he can judiciously interchange subjects and thereby make the treatment groups more nearly equal with respect to means and also variances. He proceeds to do so. What are the consequences of this action?

It is true that a comparison of the group means on the dependent variable may now be subject to a smaller error than was true of the original random arrangement, but there is something more to be considered. The experimenter has, in a particular total sample of subjects, a certain amount of error variability.   Contriving an arrangement having equal, or nearly equal, means has the effect of simultaneously enlarging the error sum of squares.   That is to say, given a certain total variability, efforts to minimize the between-treatment variability will maximize the within-treatment variability.

The consequence is that the experimental comparison will be subject to a smaller bias but will be evaluated as if it were subject to a larger bias.   In the long run, differences between means will vary less, but the variance of the differences will be estimated as if they varied more.   The supposed advantage of the equalization is thus lost in the evaluation.

The objection to this interference with the randomization of errors is that the form of the sampling distribution, which must be known in order to have a valid test of significance, cannot be determined.

A similar kind of fallacious matching is sometimes employed in matched-group designs.   The experimenter measures his subjects on a matching variable, ranks them, constitutes groups of the desired size, and randomly allocates the treatments to the subjects in each matched group.   If he tabulates the measures on the matching variable according to the random assignment of subjects, he will no doubt discover that the column means in the $(r \times c)$ table could be made more nearly equal by reassigning subjects in one or more groups.

Again, the consequences of this tampering with the randomization can be understood by considering the total variability and its redistribution.   The total variability is given by the selection of the total sample, and rearranging subjects within the total sample will not affect this over-all variation.   The between-group variability is fixed by the forming of groups and rearranging within a group will not affect this component.   Equalizing column or treatment means reduces the between-column variability.   This effect can only be compensated for by an increase in the error sum of squares.

Thus the rearrangement of subjects may reduce the bias in the experimental comparison, but it invalidates our estimate of that bias.   In the long run, the variance of the experimental comparison will be reduced, but estimates of that variance will be too large.   We can also say, as we did for the other case of incorrect matching, that the sampling distribution of our test of significance is indeterminate.

REFERENCES

1. Cochran, W.G., and Cox, G.M., *Experimental Designs.*   New York: John Wiley & Sons, Inc., 1950.
2. Cox, D.R., "The Use of a Concomitant Variable in Selecting an Experimental Design." *Biometrika*, 1957, 44, 150–158.

3. Feldt, L.S., "A Comparison of the Precision of Three Experimental Designs Employing a Concomitant Variable." *Psychometrika*, 1958, 23, 335–354.
4. Gourlay, N., "Covariance Analysis and Its Applications in Psychological Research." *British Journal of Statistical Psychology*, 1953, 6, 25–34.
5. Kenney, J.F., and Keeping, E.S., *Mathematics of Statistics*. New York: D. Van Nostrand Co., Inc., 1951.
6. Teichroew, D., "Tables of Expected Values of Order Statistics and Products of Order Statistics for Samples of Size Twenty and Less from the Normal Distribution." *Annals of Mathematical Statistics*, 1956, 27, 410–426.

APPENDIX

Table A*

Values of F equaled or exceeded by 0.05 of the values in the sampling distribution. The Table can be used, when the 0.05 level of significance is desired, in testing treatment effects, regression in analysis of covariance, and homogeneity of regressions in analysis of covariance.

df for variance in numerator

	1	2	3	4	5	6	7
4	7.71	6.94	6.59	6.39	6.26	6.16	6.09
5	6.61	5.79	5.41	5.19	5.05	4.95	4.88
6	5.99	5.14	4.76	4.53	4.39	4.28	4.21
7	5.59	4.74	4.35	4.12	3.97	3.87	3.79
8	5.32	4.46	4.07	3.84	3.69	3.58	3.50
9	5.12	4.26	3.86	3.63	3.48	3.37	3.29
10	4.96	4.10	3.71	3.48	3.33	3.22	3.14
11	4.84	3.98	3.59	3.36	3.20	3.09	3.01
12	4.75	3.89	3.49	3.26	3.11	3.00	2.91
13	4.67	3.81	3.41	3.18	3.03	2.92	2.83
14	4.60	3.74	3.34	3.11	2.96	2.85	2.76
15	4.54	3.68	3.29	3.06	2.90	2.79	2.71
16	4.49	3.63	3.24	3.01	2.85	2.74	2.66
17	4.45	3.59	3.20	2.96	2.81	2.70	2.61
18	4.41	3.55	3.16	2.93	2.77	2.66	2.58
19	4.38	3.52	3.13	2.90	2.74	2.63	2.54
20	4.35	3.49	3.10	2.87	2.71	2.60	2.51
21	4.32	3.47	3.07	2.84	2.68	2.57	2.49
22	4.30	3.44	3.05	2.82	2.66	2.55	2.46
23	4.28	3.42	3.03	2.80	2.64	2.53	2.44
24	4.26	3.40	3.01	2.78	2.62	2.51	2.42
25	4.24	3.39	2.99	2.76	2.60	2.49	2.40
30	4.17	3.32	2.92	2.69	2.53	2.42	2.33
40	4.08	3.23	2.84	2.61	2.45	2.34	2.25

df for variance in denominator

Interpolation may be performed using reciprocals of the degrees of freedom.

* This table is abridged from Merrington and Thompson's "Tables of Percentage Points of the Inverted Beta Distribution," *Biometrika*, 33, 1943, p. 73. It is printed here with permission of the Trustees of *Biometrika*.

Table B*

Values of F equaled or exceeded by 0.025 of the values in the sampling distribution.

If, in testing the homogeneity of two sample variances, the larger variance is placed over the smaller, the number of ratios greater than any given value (equal to or greater than unity) is doubled. Therefore use of the values tabled below, in comparing two sample variances, will provide a 0.05 level of significance.

df for larger variance (numerator)

		4	5	6	7	8	9	10	12	15	20
	4	9.60	9.36	9.20	9.07	8.98	8.90	8.84	8.75	8.66	8.56
	5	7.39	7.15	6.98	6.85	6.76	6.68	6.62	6.52	6.43	6.33
df	6	6.23	5.99	5.82	5.70	5.60	5.52	5.46	5.37	5.27	5.17
for	7	5.52	5.29	5.12	4.99	4.90	4.82	4.76	4.67	4.57	4.47
smaller	8	5.05	4.82	4.65	4.53	4.43	4.36	4.30	4.20	4.10	4.00
variance	9	4.72	4.48	4.32	4.20	4.10	4.03	3.96	3.87	3.77	3.67
(denomi-	10	4.47	4.24	4.07	3.95	3.85	3.78	3.72	3.62	3.52	3.42
nator)	12	4.12	3.89	3.73	3.61	3.51	3.44	3.37	3.28	3.18	3.07
	15	3.80	3.58	3.41	3.29	3.20	3.12	3.06	2.96	2.86	2.76
	20	3.51	3.29	3.13	3.01	2.91	2.84	2.77	2.68	2.57	2.46

Interpolation may be performed using reciprocals of the degrees of freedom.

* This table is abridged from Merrington and Thompson's "Tables of Percentage Points of the Inverted Beta Distribution," *Biometrika*, 33, 1943, p. 73.   It is published here with permission of the Trustees of *Biometrika*.

Table C*

Values of chi square equaled or exceeded by 0.05 of the values in the sampling distribution.

In using the values for Bartlett's test of homogeneity of sample variances, $df = c - 1$, where c = number of samples.

In using the values for the test in which we combine probabilities from independent experiments, $df = 2e$ where e = the number of experiments.

df	χ^2
1	3.841
2	5.991
3	7.815
4	9.488
5	11.070
6	12.592
7	14.067
8	15.507
9	16.919
10	18.307

* Table C is abridged from Table III of Fisher: *Statistical Methods for Research Workers*, published by Oliver and Boyd Ltd., Edinburgh, by permission of the author and publishers.

INDEX